Written by

Michelle Powers, Teri Barenborg, Tari Sexton, and Lauren Monroe

Editor: Christie Weltz
Designer/Production: Tawney Johnson
Art Director: Moonhee Pak
Project Director: Stacey Faulkner

DEDICATION

This book is dedicated to all of the educators and children who have inspired us to make education a hands-on experience and, most importantly, instilled within us a lifelong love of learning.

ACKNOWLEDGMENTS

First and foremost, we would like to thank our families and friends who have supported us in so many ways—from the steadfast support of our chosen career path and passion all the way through the inspiration and creation of this series of books. Each of us has an amazing support system that has not only encouraged us but also made it possible for us to devote our time to this project. A sincere thank-you to our colleagues, both past and present, as well as all the educators who have inspired us to create a collection of lessons that encourage students to grow and take ownership of their learning. Without the continued support and encouragement of our dear friend Lynn Howard, these books would not have been possible.

Our school district, St. Lucie Public Schools, known for being the first Kids at Hope school district in the state of Florida, motivated us to build a culture of learning where students state daily that "All children are capable of success. No exceptions." This mindset, along with the work of Carol Dweck and her focus on self-efficacy through a growth mindset, has inspired us to develop lessons that encourage problem solving and perseverance, allowing students to learn from their mistakes.

We would like to thank the various teachers who have opened their doors to us and, more importantly, the students in those classrooms who have tested these exciting lessons during their development. These teachers have allowed us to model, motivate, and encourage them to transition from the "Sage on the Stage" to a "Guide on the Side," giving students the opportunity to drive their own learning.

FOREWORD

Science instruction has changed. Many of us can remember the traditional lecture and note giving model of instruction that had been used for years. I was very alone in my middle school earth science classroom and had no support, no textbook, and no curriculum guide. Living day to day with content that was totally unfamiliar to me, I taught the same way to all students and didn't realize that many of them were not engaged or learning. I had to change and allow for more engagement, exploration, and experimentation. It quickly became the way I taught, and students benefited from the problem solving, collaboration, and inquiry-based activities. When I began my science teaching career years ago, I would have appreciated a resource that provided me with a set of classroom lessons that would challenge and motivate my students.

The Next Generation Science Standards are placing a great emphasis on how we "do science" in the classroom. The integration of science, technology, engineering, arts, and math (STEAM) provides multiple opportunities to include problem solving, engineering practices, and literacy while engaging and motivating students in real-world science experiences.

I really like this book. These lessons are perfect for any teacher who may or may not feel comfortable with teaching science. I really like that the lessons are aligned with the 5E Instructional Model (engage, explore, explain, elaborate, and evaluate). Teachers who use the lessons will address the 5E model and challenge their students with the engineering process. The authors are a team of educators who understand how to teach science. Their teaching has evolved from a traditional approach to becoming facilitators of science knowledge. Teri, Lauren, Michelle, and Tari have spent time learning about the changes in science education and how to design effective science classroom environments. As a professional development associate, I spent three years with them as they explored how to create a balanced science program focused on the Next Generation Science Standards. They invested a large amount of time researching what works and implementing those best practices in their classrooms. I have had the opportunity to be in all of their classrooms and see the engagement and excitement as students collaborate on real-world engineering design problems. The teachers continually reinforce the idea that their students ARE scientists and must practice the habits of scientists. A by-product of these teachers' efforts is a book that other teachers can use today in their classrooms to make it exciting to teach and learn about science!

I am honored that Teri, Lauren, Michelle, and Tari asked me to write the foreword for their book. These teachers truly live and breathe quality science teaching and learning. Their passion, dedication, and commitment to effective science instruction make the activities and ideas in this book invaluable to anyone who wants to get excited about STEAM in their classroom.

Lynn F. Howard
Author and Professional Development Associate
Five Easy Steps to a Balanced Science Program

TABLE OF CONTENTS

GETTING STARTED

Introduction 5
How to Use this Book 6
The Standards 13
Integration in the Engineering
Design Challenge 14
STEAM Design Process 15
Recording Information
in a Science Notebook 16

EARTH AND SPACE SCIENCE

STEAM for the Fall 20
STEAM for the Winter 26
STEAM for the Spring 32
STEAM for the Summer 38
Twinkle, Twinkle, Where Are the Stars? 44

ENGINEERING DESIGN

As Time Goes By 50
Deflated Developments 56
Geo World 62
To Get to the Other Side 68
Tremendous Towers 74

LIFE SCIENCE

Air Bowling 80
Bears Build Barriers 86
Can It Stand Alone? 92
Must Find My Mama 98

PHYSICAL SCIENCE

Cavernous Communication 104
Rapunzel, Your Prince Is Calling 110
So You Think Rice Can Dance? 116
The Napping Pod 122

APPENDIX

Lesson Plan-Specific Reproducibles 129
Individual Blueprint Design Sheet 143
Group Blueprint Design Sheet 144
Vocabulary Sheet 145
What I Learned 146
STEAM Job Cards 147
Science Notebook Cover 148
STEAM Rubric 149
Bibliography 151

INTRODUCTION

Science, technology, engineering, art, and math work together to make learning fun!

The Next Generation Science Standards place a greater emphasis on science, technology, engineering, arts, and math (STEAM) in today's classrooms. Schools are implementing and encouraging strong STEAM programs in classrooms in order to provide critical thinking lessons that meet the content standards. STEAM lessons should include problem-solving skills, enhance learning across various disciplines, promote student inquiry, and engage students with real-world situations. Students should be exposed to careers in the STEAM fields and develop skills such as communication, data analysis, following a process, designing a product, and argumentation based on evidence, all while cementing effective collaboration techniques that are necessary for a successful career in STEAM fields.

The lessons in this book are intended to support teachers in implementing the engineering design process in their classroom while integrating national standards from other disciplines. In the engineering design process, teachers become a facilitator rather than the instructional focus. Teachers encourage and guide students to work as a team to find a creative solution without providing step-by-step instructions. The engineering design process shifts away from the long-standing process of the scientific method by placing more emphasis on inquiry. Students are inspired to act as scientists and engineers through the use of sketches, diagrams, mathematical relationships, and literacy connections. By creating their very own models and products based on background information from their studies, students are immediately engaged through a meaningful, rewarding lesson.

Each lesson begins by presenting students with a design challenge scenario, or hook, in order to immediately excite students with a real-world situation that they are on a mission to solve. Students are then given a dilemma, mission, and blueprint design sheet and are asked to collaborate with team members to create several prototypes. Teams are required to choose one prototype to present to their teacher before gathering materials and constructing the chosen design. After testing out their design, teams take part in a class discussion and modify their ideas for redesign and improvement of their prototype. Finally, teams are asked to create a justification piece in order to sell their new prototype. Suggestions for justification projects are provided for each design challenge and include writing a persuasive letter, creating an advertisement or presentation, recording a video, or any other creative ideas they come up with in response to the challenge.

The engaging STEAM design challenge lessons in this book

- Promote analytical and reflective thinking

- Enhance learning across various disciplines

- Encourage students to collaborate to solve real-world design challenges

- Integrate national standards

- Are classroom tested

HOW TO USE THIS BOOK

STEAM design challenges follow the engineering practices that have become recently known in the education field. Engineering practices teach students to solve a problem by designing, creating, and justifying their design. With this model in mind, teachers shift from a "giver of information" to a "facilitator of knowledge." Instead of leading children to the right conclusion through experimental steps, the teacher allows them to work through the process themselves, often changing their plan to improve their original design.

STEAM design challenges allow art to support and enhance the learning of science and math while the engineering process is followed. Students will often use, or be encouraged to use, technology to facilitate their learning. The teacher's role as facilitator allows him or her to guide student thinking by asking questions instead of giving answers. Each lesson covers cross-curricular standards and supports teacher planning for collaboration with other teachers.

Typically, science is not taught as often in elementary school as English, reading, writing, and math, so assignments have been included within the lessons that will assist in giving students skills and practice in those other key subjects.

Lessons focus on key national science standards that are required for many standardized tests and include core English language arts and math standards. National engineering standards as well as national arts and national technology standards are also included in the lessons.

The 5E Instructional Model emphasizes building new ideas using existing knowledge. The components of this model—*Engage, Explore, Explain, Elaborate,* and *Evaluate*—are also a key design feature in the structure of each design challenge. Each design challenge requires the students to respond using mathematical, written, oral, and theatrical skills that are developmentally appropriate while working through each phase of the 5E model.

PHASES OF THE 5E MODEL

ENGAGE
Students make connections between past and present learning and focus their thinking on learning outcomes in the activity.

EXPLORE
Students continue to build on their knowledge of their learning through exploration and manipulation of materials.

EXPLAIN
Students support their understanding of the concepts through verbal or written communication. This is also a time when students may demonstrate new skills and when teachers can introduce new vocabulary.

ELABORATE
Students extend their understanding of concepts by obtaining more information about a topic through new experiences.

EVALUATE
Students assess their understanding of key concepts and skills.

LESSON PLAN FORMAT

Each lesson centers around the Design Challenge Purpose and has two distinct sections—Setting the Stage and STEAM in Action.

- **Setting the Stage** provides an overview of the lesson, suggested time frame, the background knowledge needed for the teacher and students as well as the standards, target vocabulary, and materials needed.

- **STEAM in Action** outlines the step-by-step procedure for implementing the lesson.

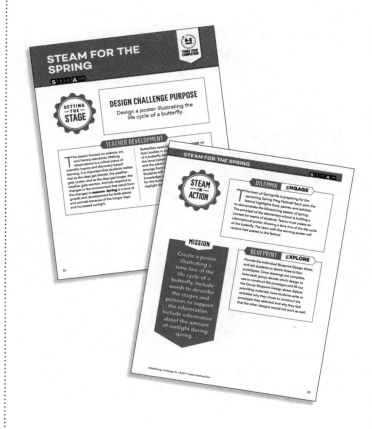

LESSON PLAN COMPONENTS

SETTING THE STAGE

Header: This section includes the title, suggested time frame for completing the lesson, and the STEAM acronym, in which the capital letters denote the main disciplines that are highlighted in each particular lesson.

Time: A suggested approximate total time for completing each lesson is provided. Because the amount of time teachers have to teach science varies within different states, districts, schools, and even grade levels, you may need to break up the lesson into smaller segments over the course of several days. Natural breaks occur between design and construction, between construction and testing, and between testing and justification.

You may choose to use the lesson ideas in the Student Development section to deepen prior knowledge or you may have your students use the literacy connections and any reputable websites you are familiar with. The lesson ideas in the Justification section are included as an optional extension of the core lesson. None of the activities before or after the core lesson are included in the time estimates. Refer to the suggested lesson timeline on page 11.

Design Challenge Purpose: This is the statement that sets the stage for the design challenge and outlines student objectives and expectations for what they should learn by completing the design challenge.

Teacher Development: This section provides background information about the science content being addressed in the lesson. Information included assists the teacher in understanding key science concepts. We understand that professional development at the elementary teacher level is often geared toward instructional delivery instead of content, especially in the content area of science. This section is provided to help support teachers who may not be as familiar with science content.

Student Development: This section contains a description of the concepts students will need to understand to complete the design challenge successfully. A link to the STEAM Dreamers website, which has active web links and additional suggested lesson ideas for deepening students' understanding of relevant science concepts, can be found on the inside front cover of this book.

Standards: This section lists specific standards for science, technology, engineering, art, math, and English language arts, along with the science and engineering practices and crosscutting concepts. These standards may apply to the activities in the challenges or in the justifications that follow. Please make sure that you review the standards for each of the lessons. The website for each set of standards is listed on page 13.

Target Vocabulary: This section lists target vocabulary to support and enhance the lesson content and to deepen students' understanding of the terms. These vocabulary terms are related to the academic content that the design challenge focuses on; can be used throughout the design challenge when in group discussion; and are an integral component of the standards covered in the challenge. Reviewing the target vocabulary prior to beginning the design challenge is recommended as students need to apply their knowledge of the science concepts and target vocabulary when solving the challenges. Ultimately, the target vocabulary should be revisited multiple times throughout the lesson.

Materials: This section lists materials and equipment that have been selected for the lessons. All materials are meant to be easy to find, inexpensive to purchase, recycled, or commonly available for free. Substitute with similar items if you have them on hand, or visit www.SteamDreamers.com for substitute suggestions.

Literacy Connections: This section lists books or articles that are meant to be used with students prior to the design challenge in order to strengthen their background knowledge and to enhance the integration of literacy in STEAM. These connections can be used during the daily classroom reading block, during small and/or whole-group instruction.

Current literacy connections for each lesson can be accessed through our website: www.SteamDreamers.com.

⚙ STEAM IN ACTION ⚙

The Dilemma: This section includes a unique real-world dilemma or scenario that hooks the students and gets them excited to solve the problem. The dilemma may include a plausible circumstance or a wild story designed to make them think. When planning the design of their prototype, student should ask themselves questions such as *Who is the client? What do we need to create? What is the purpose of the creation? What is the ultimate goal?* Students should discuss these questions with other members of their team and record their responses in their science notebooks.

Note: This is the Engage portion of the lesson, as outlined in the 5E Instructional Model.

The Mission: This section includes the defined challenge statement. This is ultimately the goal that the students are trying to reach.

Blueprint Design: This section instructs students on how to focus their thinking in order to solve the problem. Individual team members design their own plans for prototypes and list the pros and cons of their designs. Each team member reviews the Blueprint Design Sheet of every other team member and records the pros and cons he or she sees. The team then chooses which member's design it will move forward with. This is where students have the opportunity to discuss and make decisions based on their analysis on the Individual Blueprint Design Sheets. Students are allowed and encouraged to add their artistic touches to their thinking. Individual and Group Blueprint Design Sheets are found in the Appendix.

Note: This is the Explore portion of the lesson, as outlined in the 5E Instructional Model.

Engineering Design Process: In this section of the lesson, teams will take their group's selected prototype through the engineering design process to create, test, analyze, and redesign as necessary until they have successfully completed their mission.

- The first step in the process is the Engineering Task in which teams will engineer their prototype.

- Students will then test their prototype based upon the mission statement.

- The analysis of their testing will include data collection and determination of success.

- The Redesign and Retest cycle will continue until the team has successfully completed the mission.

Helpful Tips: In this section you'll find suggestions designed to address common issues that may arise during the design challenges. Some tips are geared toward the steps in the engineering design process, and some are more lesson-specific.

Reflections: This section provides suggestions for reflective questions to ask students to help guide and facilitate their thinking at various stages within the engineering design process. It is recommended that students record these questions and their reflections in a science notebook. See pages 16–19 for more information on using a science notebook.

Note: This is the Explain and Elaborate portion of the lesson, as outlined in the 5E Instructional Model.

Justification: This is the stage of the lesson where students apply what they learned in a meaningful and creative way through different mediums, such as technology and the arts. These justifications can occur in many forms: a formal letter, an advertisement, a poem, a jingle, a skit, or a technology-enhanced presentation.

Note: This is the Evaluate portion of the lesson, as outlined in the 5E Instructional Model.

SUGGESTED LESSON TIMELINE

Lesson Progression:

1. Teacher Development/Student Development/Literacy Connections

2. Dilemma/Mission/Blueprint Design

3. Engineering Task/Test Trial/Analyze/ Redesign/Reflection

4. Justification

If the lesson will be spread out over multiple days:

Day 1: Teacher Development/Student Development/Literacy Connections

Day 2: Dilemma/Mission/Blueprint Design

Day 3: Engineering Task/Test Trial

Days 4–6: Analyze/Redesign/Reflection (Can be spread over 3 days)

Days 7–8: Justification

THE APPENDIX

Lesson-Specific Activity Pages: Some lessons include specific activity pages for enhancing or completing the design challenges. They are found in the Appendix section.

Blueprint Design Sheets: Every lesson requires students to first use the Individual Blueprint Design Sheet to create and list the pros and cons of their and their teammates' designs. Students will discuss their designs with team members and choose one design to use for building their prototype. This design, and reasons why it was chosen, are recorded on the Group Blueprint Design Sheet.

Rubric: A rubric for grading the STEAM challenges is included. This rubric focuses on the engineering process. However, it does not include a means to assess the justification components.

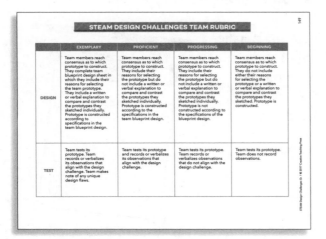

STEAM Job Cards: If your students are struggling with the collaboration process, try assigning them specific roles. Assigning students jobs often helps them better collaborate by giving them guidelines to follow. Suggestions for jobs are provided on the STEAM Job Cards found in the Appendix. Four students per team is recommended.

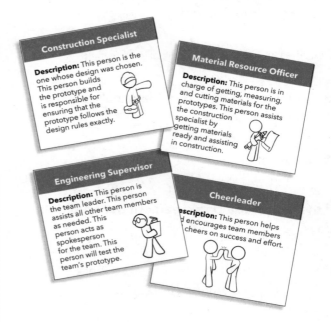

THE STANDARDS

SCIENCE

www.nextgenscience.org/search-standards-dci
The Next Generation Science Standards are arranged by disciplinary core ideas (DCI). When accessing these standards, search by standard and DCI. The standards are identified in the lessons by grade level and DCI. (e.g., 5-ESS3-1–Grade 5, Earth and Human Activity, Standard 1).

TECHNOLOGY

www.iste.org/standards
The International Society for Technology in Education (ISTE) publishes the national technology standards. Each of the standards is categorized into four main categories.

1. Creativity and innovation
2. Communication and collaboration
3. Research and information fluency
4. Critical thinking, problem solving, and decision making

Within each of these categories there are more specific indicators that are identified by a letter. Standards within the lessons will be indicated by the category (e.g., ISTE.1).

ENGINEERING

www.nextgenscience.org/search-standards-dci
The Next Generation Science Standards identify the engineering standards as well. They are categorized by the grade band of 3-5 (e.g., 3-5-ETS1-1).

ARTS

www.nationalartsstandards.org
www.corestandards.org/ELA-Literacy

The National Core Arts Standards are divided into four categories:

1. Creating
2. Performing/Presenting/Producing
3. Responding
4. Connecting

Each of these categories contains anchor standards. Within the lesson, the standards will be identified by the category and the anchor standard (e.g., Creating, Anchor Standard #1).

In addition to performance standards, the literacy standards are embedded throughout the lessons. Each lesson identifies specific English language arts (ELA) standards (e.g., CCSS.ELA-LITERACY.W.5.2).

MATH

www.corestandards.org/math
The Common Core Math Standards are divided into two categories:

1. Content
2. Practice

The content standards are those items such as computation and geometry. The practice standards are a framework for ensuring that students are practicing math in a meaningful and appropriate manner.

The content standards will be identified first in the Math Standards column and the Math Practice Standards will be underneath (e.g., CCSS.MATH.CONTENT.5.G.A.2–real world graphing and CCSS.MATH.PRACTICE.MP.4–model with mathematics).

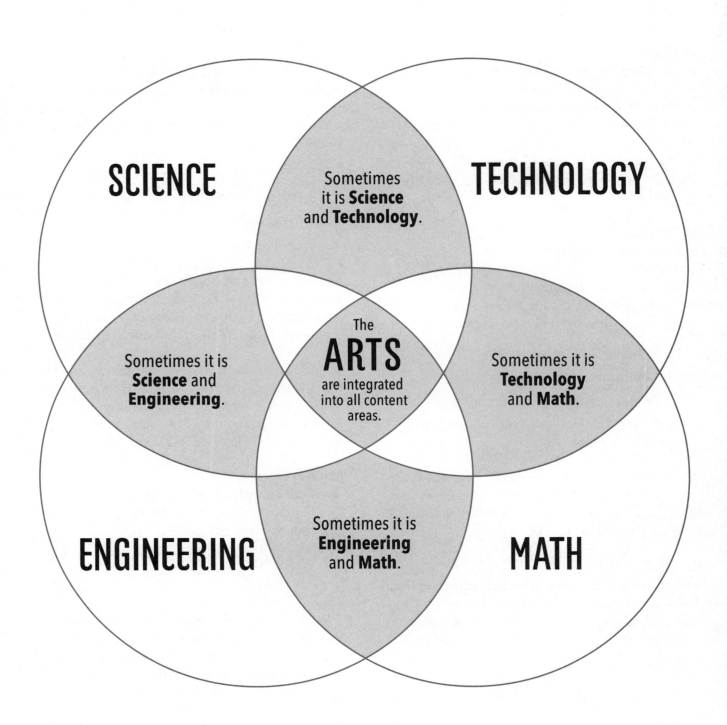

SCIENCE

TECHNOLOGY

Sometimes it is **Science** and **Technology**.

Sometimes it is **Science** and **Engineering**.

The **ARTS** are integrated into all content areas.

Sometimes it is **Technology** and **Math**.

ENGINEERING

Sometimes it is **Engineering** and **Math**.

MATH

Sometimes it is all five!

STEAM DESIGN PROCESS

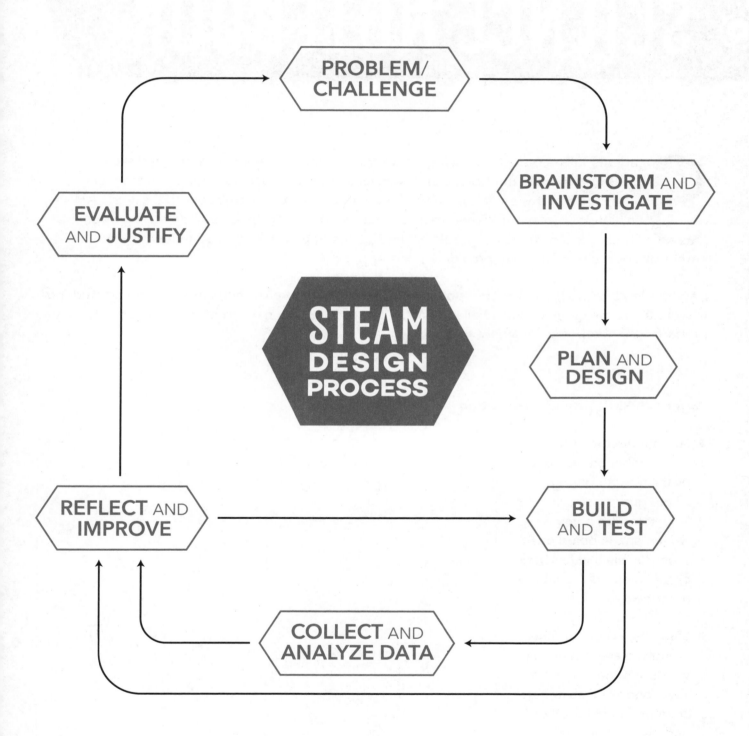

RECORDING INFORMATION IN A
SCIENCE NOTEBOOK

Students will record their thinking, answer questions, make observations, and sketch ideas as they work through each design challenge. It is recommended that teachers have students designate a section of their regular science notebooks to these STEAM challenges or have students create a separate STEAM science notebook using a spiral notebook, a composition book, or lined pages stapled together. A generic science notebook cover sheet has been provided in the Appendix.

Have students set up their notebooks based upon the natural breaks in the lesson. Remind students to write the name of the design challenge at the top of the page in their notebooks each time they prepare their notebooks for a new challenge

Pages 1–3 Background Information

- Students record notes from any information provided by the teacher during whole-group instruction (e.g., teacher's notes written on the board or a reproducible that has been cut apart and glued into the notebook).

- Students record student-friendly related vocabulary words and their definitions. Teachers may wish to have students cut out the words and their definitions to match up by gluing the pieces into their notebooks. Teachers can also provide a sheet of definitions

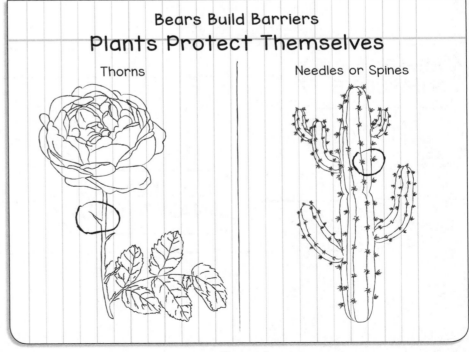

Bears Build Barriers
Plants Protect Themselves

Thorns   Needles or Spines

Page 1

Page 2

Page 3

for students to cut out and glue into their notebooks and then write the word for each definition. Or make copies of the vocabulary sheet (page 145) and have students complete it and glue it into their notebooks.

- Students record notes from research, including information from science books, diagrams, and worksheets or activities provided by the teacher. These worksheets can be completed by the students and then glued into their notebooks.

Page 4 Dilemma and Mission

- Display the dilemma and mission for students to record.

- Or make copies of the dilemma and mission for students to glue into their notebooks to use as a reference.

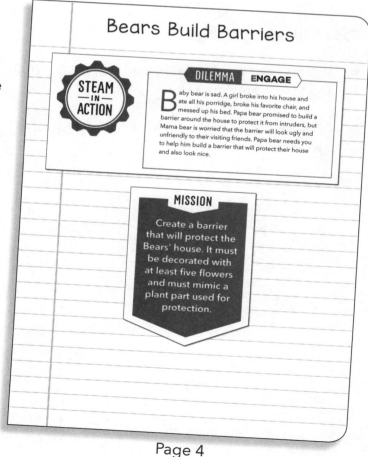

Page 4

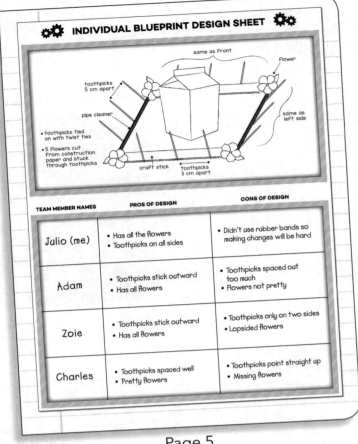

INDIVIDUAL BLUEPRINT DESIGN SHEET

TEAM MEMBER NAMES	PROS OF DESIGN	CONS OF DESIGN
Julio (me)	• Has all the flowers • Toothpicks on all sides	• Didn't use rubber bands so making changes will be hard
Adam	• Toothpicks stick outward • Has all flowers	• Toothpicks spaced out too much • Flowers not pretty
Zoie	• Toothpicks stick outward • Has all flowers	• Toothpicks only on two sides • Lopsided flowers
Charles	• Toothpicks spaced well • Pretty flowers	• Toothpicks point straight up • Missing flowers

Page 5

Page 5 Blueprint Design

● Students draw their own suggested design. Then students write the pros and cons of both their and their teammates' designs.

● Or make copies of the Individual Blueprint Design Sheet for students to complete and glue into their notebooks.

Bears Build Barriers

AFTER TEST TRIAL 1	Did your barrier prototype keep out the "intruder"? Explain. What materials did successful teams use to create their barriers?
ANALYSIS	How will you change your barrier prototype to make it more effective at keeping out the intruder?
AFTER TEST TRIAL 2	Did your barrier prototype keep out the "intruder"? Explain. What were the similarities and differences between the different teams' prototypes?
ANALYSIS	How will you change your barrier prototype to make it more effective at keeping out the "intruder"?
AFTER TEST TRIAL 3	Was your barrier successful at stopping the "intruder"? Explain. Discuss how your barrier is similar to real-world barriers that are used around homes.

Page 6

Bears Build Barriers
SUMMARY

Today we learned that plants have external structures that protect them. An example of this type of structure is a thorn on a rose bush. We tried to mimic a plant with thorns by building a barrier with sharp sticks to protect a house.

Page 7

Pages 6-7 Engineering Task, Test Trial, Analyze, Redesign

● The teacher can use the reflection questions provided for each challenge to facilitate discussion with teams during each test trial.

● Students can respond verbally to the reflection questions and to more general questions about which parts of the prototype were successful and which parts were not.

● Students can summarize what they learned during the challenge either verbally during a discussion with the teacher or in writing in their science notebooks.

STEAM FOR THE FALL

4-5 HOURS
TIME FOR COMPLETION

S t e A m

SETTING
—THE—
STAGE

DESIGN CHALLENGE PURPOSE

Design an informative book describing autumn.

TEACHER DEVELOPMENT

This lesson focuses on science, art, and literacy standards. Making observations is a critical piece of scientific inquiry and discovery-based learning. It is important for students to realize that as the days get shorter, the temperature outside gets cooler, and as the days get longer, the temperature gets warmer. Animals respond to changes in the environment caused by the changes in the seasons. Many animals **migrate** or **hibernate** in winter because of lack of food sources in cold weather. Animals that hibernate spend the autumn, or fall, months before winter eating lots of food in preparation for surviving the cold winter months.

STUDENT DEVELOPMENT

Before beginning the lesson, provide time to explore websites, videos, and literacy connections with students. Lead a discussion with students, prompting them with questions such as *What time of day do you feel the most heat outside? During the day or at night? What happens when the sun is not visible? What would* *happen if the sun didn't rise one day? Why do seasons occur and what happens to plants and animals when seasons change?*

Note: Visit the website listed on the inside front cover for videos and additional resources about the seasons.

STANDARDS

SCIENCE	TECHNOLOGY	ENGINEERING	ARTS	MATH	ELA
1-ESS1-2			Creating #1		CCSS.ELA-LITERACY.SL.1.1
			Creating #2		CCSS.ELA-LITERACY.W.1.1
			Creating #3		CCSS.ELA-LITERACY.W.1.2
			Performing/ Presenting/ Producing #4, #5, #6		CCSS.ELA-LITERACY.W.1.8

SCIENCE & ENGINEERING PRACTICES

Planning and Carrying Out Investigations: Make observations (firsthand or from media) to collect data that can be used to make comparisons.

CROSSCUTTING CONCEPTS

Patterns: Patterns in the natural world can be observed, used to describe phenomena, and used as evidence.

TARGET VOCABULARY

autumn

daylight

heat

hibernate

migrate

MATERIALS

- crayons
- colored pencils
- construction paper
- empty cereal boxes
- magazines
- glue
- tape
- fall book map (page 129)

LITERACY CONNECTIONS

Time to Sleep
by Denise Fleming

The Reasons for Seasons
by Gail Gibbons

Four Seasons Make a Year
by Anne Rockwell

NOTES

DILEMMA — ENGAGE

Chip and Squeak, two young chipmunks, were out playing in the forest when their mother was scooped up by a hawk! They knew the time would come when they would need to fend for themselves and prepare for the changing seasons, but they could not remember the signs their mother had taught them to look for to help them get ready for winter and the hibernation season. Should they start gathering food now? Was it too early? Did they have enough time to prepare? Please help Chip and Squeak by creating an informational book about autumn.

MISSION

Create a book about the autumn season.

Include the following:

- at least 5 pages
- at least 1 fact and 1 illustration per page
- information about the signs in nature that show that autumn is beginning
- information about the amount of daylight hours during this season

BLUEPRINT — EXPLORE

Provide the book map design sheet (page 129), and have students sketch information that they want to include in the team book about autumn. Have each team decide which ideas from teammates' design sheets they should use for the book. Before gathering materials, teams must explain why they included the information they chose for the book and why they believe the other information and designs would not work as well.

ENGINEERING TASK

Each team will design an informational book that describes the autumn season. The book should include background information and illustrations.

Note: Give students the book map. Tell them to sketch pictures and write no more than 10 words for each page in their book.

TEST TRIAL

Each team will read its book to another team and participate in a question and answer session.

Note: Remind students to discuss how the vocabulary terms *daylight*, *heat*, *hibernation*, and *migration* were incorporated into their books.

ANALYZE

Teams will discuss some of the successful parts of their books and parts in need of improvement.

Teams should be allowed to observe the other designs to gather ideas, reflect, and make changes in order to improve their books.

REDESIGN

Teams can make adjustments to their books.

HELPFUL TIPS

- After the Test Trial, have teams take a gallery walk to view other teams' designs for possible ideas to assist them in the Analyze and Redesign portions of the engineering design process.

- If teams are successful on the first try, encourage them to make their prototypes even more efficient. If it is a scenario in which this is not feasible, distribute team members to other teams to be a support for them in making their prototypes more efficient. Alternatively, at teacher discretion, move students on to the Justification portion of the lesson.

- If after the third test the final prototype is still unsuccessful, have students write how they would start over. These challenges are meant to have students build on what they originally designed. If the design proved to be unsuccessful, encourage a reflection/justification on what they would do if they were allowed to start again from scratch.

STEAM Design Challenges Gr. 1 © 2017 Creative Teaching Press

REFLECTIONS — EXPLAIN & ELABORATE

AFTER TEST TRIAL 1	Did you answer all of the questions asked by the audience after reading your book aloud? Did all members of your team participate?
ANALYSIS	What could you add to your book to make it more informative?
AFTER TEST TRIAL 2	Did you include illustrations and information about preparations for autumn and how animals can tell autumn is coming?
ANALYSIS	Were you able to answer all questions asked by your classmates or do you need to find more information?
AFTER TEST TRIAL 3	What did your classmates learn from your book? What was your favorite part of the challenge?

JUSTIFICATION — EVALUATE

ARTS — Create a front cover for your book. Use pictures from magazines, photographs, and other art materials.

STEAM FOR THE WINTER

4-5 HOURS

TIME FOR COMPLETION

S t E A m

SETTING —THE— STAGE

DESIGN CHALLENGE PURPOSE

Build a habitat diorama representing a place where an animal could hibernate during the long winter months.

TEACHER DEVELOPMENT

This lesson focuses on science, engineering, art, and literacy standards. It is important for students to realize that as the days get shorter, the temperature gets cooler, and as days get longer, the temperature warms up. Animals respond to changes in the environment that result from changes in seasons. Many animals **hibernate**, or spend the winter resting, because they lack food sources in cold weather. In winter, it is crucial for many animals to find a location to hibernate in order to **survive**.

Note: We chose animals for this challenge that hibernate differently. Be sure to do some research on the hibernation of those particular species before this lesson.

STUDENT DEVELOPMENT

Before beginning the lesson, provide time to explore websites, videos, and literacy connections with students. Review **hibernation** and discuss different animals that hibernate and why this is so important to their survival.

Some animals go into hibernation to make it through freezing cold weather or a time when very little food is available to them. During this time, their breathing and heart rate slow or, in some cases, even stop. Animals do this in order to conserve energy. Some animals hibernate for just a few days, while others can hibernate for months! These animals can be found hibernating in logs, trees, caves, cocoons, or (in the case of pet hamsters) even in your home, when it gets too cold!

Note: Visit the website listed on the inside front cover for additional resources about the seasons.

STANDARDS

SCIENCE	TECHNOLOGY	ENGINEERING	ARTS	MATH	ELA
1-ESS1-2		K-2-ETS1-1	Creating #1		CCSS.ELA-LITERACY.SL.1.1
		K-2-ETS1-2	Creating #2		CCSS.ELA-LITERACY.W.1.1
		K-2-ETS1-3	Creating #3		CCSS.ELA-LITERACY.W.1.2
			Performing/Presenting/Producing #4, #5, #6		CCSS.ELA-LITERACY.W.1.8

SCIENCE & ENGINEERING PRACTICES

Planning and Carrying Out Investigations: Make observations (firsthand or from media) to collect data that can be used to make comparisons.

CROSSCUTTING CONCEPTS

Patterns: Patterns in the natural world can be observed, used to describe phenomena, and used as evidence.

TARGET VOCABULARY

daylight

heat

hibernate

survive

winter

MATERIALS

- shoe box
- crayons
- colored pencils
- modeling clay
- craft sticks
- construction paper
- empty cereal boxes
- magazines
- glue
- tape
- scissors

LITERACY CONNECTIONS

Bear Snores On
by Karma Wilson

Hibernation Station
by Michelle Meadows

NOTES

STEAM —IN— ACTION

DILEMMA — ENGAGE

Brrr, it's cold out there! Winter is upon us, and that means it is time for some animals to find a place to rest and keep warm until warmer spring days return. Buddy Bear, Susie Squirrel, Henry Hedgehog, Toby Turtle, and Freddy Frog all need to find a place to settle down and rest until the cold winter weather passes. Can you design a habitat where one of these animals could hibernate?

MISSION

Create a diorama that represents the real habitat for one animal to hibernate in during winter. Include on an index card a note about how much sunlight shines in the habitat during the winter, and attach it to the back of the diorama.

BLUEPRINT — EXPLORE

Provide the Individual Blueprint Design sheet, and ask students to sketch three to four prototypes. Once drawings are complete, have each group decide which design to use to construct the prototype and fill out the Group Blueprint Design sheet. Before providing materials, have students write or verbalize why they chose to construct the prototype they selected and why they feel that the other designs would not work as well.

ENGINEERING TASK   **TEST TRIAL**   **ANALYZE** **REDESIGN**

ENGINEERING TASK	TEST TRIAL	ANALYZE	REDESIGN
Each team will construct a habitat diorama that represents a place where an animal could hibernate during winter. *Note:* Teacher should assign a different animal to each group.	Each team will present its habitat diorama to another team and then answer questions about it. *Note:* You may want to provide students with question stems using the target vocabulary to help them in their question and answer sessions.	Teams will discuss some of the successful parts of their dioramas and parts in need of improvement. Teams should be allowed to observe the other dioramas to gather ideas and make changes to improve their dioramas.	Teams can use a colored pencil to make adjustments to their original design sketches.

HELPFUL TIPS

- After the Test Trial, have teams take a gallery walk to view other teams' designs for possible ideas to assist them in the Analyze and Redesign portions of the engineering design process.

- If teams are successful on the first try, encourage them to make their prototypes even more efficient. If it is a scenario in which this is not feasible, distribute team members to other teams to be a support for them in making their prototypes more efficient. Alternatively, at teacher discretion, move students on to the Justification portion of the lesson.

- If after the third test the final prototype is still unsuccessful, have students write how they would start over. These challenges are meant to have students build on what they originally designed. If the design proved to be unsuccessful, encourage a reflection/justification on what they would do if they were allowed to start again from scratch.

REFLECTIONS   EXPLAIN & ELABORATE

AFTER TEST TRIAL 1	Did you answer all of the questions asked by the other team? Did all members of your team participate?
ANALYSIS	What could you add to your diorama to make it more realistic for your animal hibernating for the winter?
AFTER TEST TRIAL 2	Did you include plants and other details that can really be found in the animal's habitat?
ANALYSIS	Were you able to answer all of the questions asked by the other team?
AFTER TEST TRIAL 3	What did your classmates learn from your presentation? What was your favorite part of the challenge?

JUSTIFICATION   EVALUATE

ELA	Write a story describing how your animal found and prepared the perfect location to hibernate for the winter.

STEAM FOR THE SPRING

4-5 HOURS

TIME FOR COMPLETION

SETTING —THE— STAGE

DESIGN CHALLENGE PURPOSE

Design a poster illustrating the life cycle of a butterfly.

TEACHER DEVELOPMENT

This lesson focuses on science, art, and literacy standards. Making observations is a critical piece of scientific inquiry and discovery-based learning. It is important that students realize that as the days get shorter, the weather gets cooler, and as the days get longer, the weather gets warmer. Animals respond to changes in the environment that result from the changes in **seasons**. **Spring** is a time of growth and development for both plants and animals because of the longer days and increased sunlight.

Butterflies need lots of sunlight to heat up their bodies in order to fly. The life cycle of a butterfly has four stages: the egg, the larva (caterpillar), the pupa (chrysalis), and the adult butterfly. Butterflies start to emerge from their chrysalises in the spring. Students will need some background knowledge of the need for heat and light for the butterflies and the amount of daylight during this time of year.

STUDENT DEVELOPMENT

Before beginning the lesson, provide time to explore websites, videos, and literacy connections with students. Lead a discussion with students, prompting them with questions such as *What time of day do you feel the most heat outside, during the day or at night? What happens when the sun is not visible? Why do seasons occur and what happens to plants and animals when seasons change?*

Lesson Idea: Students can decorate a small flower pot and plant grass seeds. Leave the potted grass seeds near sunlight and allow students to water and track the growth of their grass over several weeks. Discuss the importance of sunlight in the growth of the grass.

Teacher can purchase butterfly eggs or caterpillars and care for them inside an enclosure in the classroom so students can observe the butterfly's life cycle.

Note: Visit the website listed on the inside front cover for additional resources about the seasons.

STANDARDS

SCIENCE	TECHNOLOGY	ENGINEERING	ARTS	MATH	ELA
1-ESS1-2			Creating #1		CCSS.ELA-LITERACY.SL.1.1
			Creating #2		CCSS.ELA-LITERACY.W.1.1
			Creating #3		CCSS.ELA-LITERACY.W.1.2
			Performing/ Presenting/ Producing #4, #5, #6		CCSS.ELA-LITERACY.W.1.8

SCIENCE & ENGINEERING PRACTICES

Planning and Carrying Out Investigations: Make observations (firsthand or from media) to collect data that can be used to make comparisons.

CROSSCUTTING CONCEPTS

Patterns: Patterns in the natural world can be observed, used to describe phenomena, and used as evidence.

TARGET VOCABULARY

daylight
heat
seasons
spring
survive

MATERIALS

- poster board
- crayons
- colored pencils
- construction paper
- empty cereal boxes
- magazines
- glue
- tape
- festival tickets (page 130)

LITERACY CONNECTIONS

The Very Hungry Caterpillar
by Eric Carle

Spring Is Here
by Mary Packard

Poppleton in Spring
by Cynthia Rylant

NOTES

STEAM
—IN—
ACTION

DILEMMA ENGAGE

The town of Springville is preparing for the upcoming Spring Fling Festival! Each year, the festival highlights food, games, and exhibits to demonstrate the blossoming season of spring. The principal of the elementary school is holding a contest for teams of students. Teams must create an informational poster showing a time line of the life cycle of the butterfly. The team with the winning poster will receive free passes to the festival.

MISSION

Create a poster illustrating a time line of the life cycle of a butterfly. Include words to describe the stages and pictures to support the information. Include information about the amount of sunlight during spring.

BLUEPRINT EXPLORE

Provide the Individual Blueprint Design sheet, and ask students to sketch three to four prototypes. Once drawings are complete, have each group decide which design to use to construct the prototype and fill out the Group Blueprint Design sheet. Before providing materials, have students write or verbalize why they chose to construct the prototype they selected and why they feel that the other designs would not work as well.

ENGINEERING TASK   **TEST TRIAL**   **ANALYZE**   **REDESIGN**

ENGINEERING TASK	TEST TRIAL	ANALYZE	REDESIGN
Each team will design a poster that illustrates the life cycle of a butterfly. The poster should include background information about each stage, illustrations, and information about the amount of hours of sunlight during the spring.	Each team will present its poster to another team and answer questions about it. *Note:* Provide question stems that include the target vocabulary for students to use during their question and answer sessions.	Teams will discuss some of the successful parts of their posters and parts in need of improvement. Teams should be allowed to observe the other poster designs to gather ideas and make changes to improve their posters.	Teams can use a colored pencil to make adjustments to their original design sketches.

HELPFUL TIPS

- After the Test Trial, have teams take a gallery walk to view other teams' designs for possible ideas to assist them in the Analyze and Redesign portions of the engineering design process.

- If teams are successful on the first try, encourage them to make their prototypes even more efficient. If it is a scenario in which this is not feasible, distribute team members to other teams to be a support for them in making their prototypes more efficient. Alternatively, at teacher discretion, move students on to the Justification portion of the lesson.

- If after the third test the final prototype is still unsuccessful, have students write how they would start over. These challenges are meant to have students build on what they originally designed. If the design proved to be unsuccessful, encourage a reflection/justification on what they would do if they were allowed to start again from scratch.

S t e A m

REFLECTIONS — EXPLAIN & ELABORATE

AFTER TEST TRIAL 1	Did you answer all of the questions asked by your classmates after your presentation? Did all members of your team participate?
ANALYSIS	What could you add to your poster to make it more informative?
AFTER TEST TRIAL 2	Did you include writing and illustrations?
ANALYSIS	Were you able to answer all of the questions asked by your classmates or do you need to find more information? Did you notice any differences between your poster and the other teams' posters?
AFTER TEST TRIAL 3	What did your classmates learn from your presentation? What was your favorite part of the challenge?

JUSTIFICATION — EVALUATE

ELA	Write a story about the life cycle of a butterfly. Explain why a butterfly might think spring is the best season.
ARTS	Create a butterfly mosaic using colored paper, paint, and newspaper.

STEAM FOR THE SUMMER

4-5 HOURS

TIME FOR COMPLETION

SETTING —THE— STAGE

DESIGN CHALLENGE PURPOSE

Design an informative book describing summer. Include safety tips for avoiding too much sun exposure.

TEACHER DEVELOPMENT

This lesson focuses on science, art, and literacy standards. Making observations is a critical piece of scientific inquiry and discovery-based learning. It is important that students realize that as the days get shorter, the temperature outside gets cooler, and as the days get longer, the temperature outside warms up. During the **summer**, many children get lots of **exposure** to the **sun** because of increased outdoor activities and longer periods of sunlight. The effects of too much sun exposure can be dangerous.

STUDENT DEVELOPMENT

Before beginning the lesson, provide time to explore websites, videos, and literacy connections with students. Lead a discussion with students, prompting them with questions such as *What time of day do you feel the most heat outside, during the day or at night? How does the temperature change in the summertime when the sun is out longer? How does exposure to the sun affect humans and animals? What can we do to protect ourselves from too much sun exposure?*

Lesson Idea: Work together to create a list of activities to do in summertime. Have students put a smiley face next to activities that can be done while staying protected from the sun.

Note: Visit the website listed on the inside front cover for more information about the seasons.

STANDARDS

SCIENCE	TECHNOLOGY	ENGINEERING	ARTS	MATH	ELA
1-ESS1-2	ISTE.3		Creating #1		CCSS.ELA-LITERACY.SL.1.1
			Creating #2		CCSS.ELA-LITERACY.W.1.1
			Creating #3		CCSS.ELA-LITERACY.W.1.2
			Performing/ Presenting/ Producing #4, #5, #6		CCSS.ELA-LITERACY.W.1.8

SCIENCE & ENGINEERING PRACTICES

Planning and Carrying Out Investigations: Make observations (firsthand or from media) to collect data that can be used to make comparisons.

CROSSCUTTING CONCEPTS

Patterns: Patterns in the natural world can be observed, used to describe phenomena, and used as evidence.

TARGET VOCABULARY

daylight

exposure

heat

summer

sun

MATERIALS

- crayons
- colored pencils
- construction paper
- empty cereal boxes
- magazines
- glue
- tape
- summer book map (page 131)

LITERACY CONNECTIONS

The Sun Is My Favorite Star
by Frank Asch

Sun Up, Sun Down
by Gail Gibbons

NOTES

DILEMMA — ENGAGE

Hooray, it's summer vacation! School is out, and it's time to enjoy the sunshine and warm weather! Mom and Dad are planning to send you and your siblings away to spend two weeks of your summer vacation with Grandma and Grandpa! During your visit, you will have time to visit fun parks, swimming pools, and beautiful beaches. But before sending you on your way, Mom and Dad want to make sure you know how to protect yourself from all of the sun exposure you will get from all those outdoor activities. Before you leave on your trip, design an informational book to show Mom and Dad that you know about summer and how to stay safe from the sun.

MISSION

Create a book about the summer season. Include safety tips for avoiding too much sun exposure. Also include information about the number of hours of sunlight during summer.

BLUEPRINT — EXPLORE

Provide the book map design sheet (page 129), and have students sketch information they want to include in the team book. Have each team decide which ideas from their teammates' design sheets they want to use for the team book. Before gathering materials, teams must explain why they included the information they chose for the book and why they believe the other information and designs will not work as well.

S T e A m

ENGINEERING TASK	TEST TRIAL	ANALYZE	REDESIGN
Each team will design an informational book that describes the summer season. The book should include background information supported by illustrations and tips to stay safe during this season.

Note: Give students the book map. Tell them to sketch pictures and write no more than 10 words for each page in their book. | Each team will read its book to another team and participate in a question and answer session.

Note: Provide the student teams with question stems using the target vocabulary. | Team members will discuss some of the successful parts of their book and parts in need of improvement.

Teams should be allowed to observe the other designs to gather ideas, reflect, and make changes in order to improve their books. | Teams can make adjustments to their books. |

HELPFUL TIPS

- After the Test Trial, have teams take a gallery walk to view other teams' designs for possible ideas to assist them in the Analyze and Redesign portions of the engineering design process.

- If teams are successful on the first try, encourage them to make their prototypes even more efficient. If it is a scenario in which this is not feasible, distribute team members to other teams to be a support for them in making their prototypes more efficient. Alternatively, at teacher discretion, move students on to the Justification portion of the lesson.

- If after the third test the final prototype is still unsuccessful, have students write how they would start over. These challenges are meant to have students build on what they originally designed. If the design proved to be unsuccessful, encourage a reflection/justification on what they would do if they were allowed to start again from scratch.

STEAM Design Challenges Gr. 1 © 2017 Creative Teaching Press

REFLECTIONS — EXPLAIN & ELABORATE

AFTER TEST TRIAL 1	Did you answer all of the questions asked by the audience after reading your book aloud? Did all members of your team participate?
ANALYSIS	What could you add to your book to make it more informative?
AFTER TEST TRIAL 2	Did you include illustrations and information about summer and how to stay safe from the sun?
ANALYSIS	Were you able to answer all of the questions asked by the audience or do you need to find more information?
AFTER TEST TRIAL 3	What did your classmates learn from your book? What was your favorite part of the challenge?

JUSTIFICATION — EVALUATE

ARTS	Create a front cover for your book. Use pictures from magazines, photographs, and other art materials.
TECHNOLOGY	Use the computer to research information about sun safety for your book. *Note:* A safe search tool for kids can be found at www.juniorsafesearch.com.

TWINKLE, TWINKLE, WHERE ARE THE STARS?

1-2 HOURS

TIME FOR COMPLETION

FOR THE MAPPING

S)T)e)A)m

SETTING —THE— STAGE

DESIGN CHALLENGE PURPOSE

Create a model of the Big Dipper.

TEACHER DEVELOPMENT

Teaching about the night sky can be difficult. However, with pictures, videos, and models, you can still help students understand that you can only observe stars in the sky at night. Most **stars** appear to move across the sky, but it is actually the movement of the earth spinning on its axis that makes the stars appear to move. We see different **constellations** in the night sky during different times of the year because of the tilt of the earth. In the fall, it is common to see Orion rise in the east and fall in the west. The **Big** and **Little Dippers (Ursa Major and Ursa Minor)** are visible in the northern hemisphere year round, because they are located in the same direction where the axis of the earth tilts toward it.

STUDENT DEVELOPMENT

Students need to learn that they can only observe stars at night. It is difficult to complete this standard during the daylight hours because the stars are not visible. This will require books, videos, and websites for students to access pictures of the night sky.

Lesson Idea: Have students use a white crayon and black construction paper to create and name their own constellation. Next, use a hole punch to punch out the spots marked with crayon, and then take turns shining a flashlight behind the constellation to project it onto a blank wall.

Note: Visit the website listed on the inside front cover for more information about stars.

STANDARDS

SCIENCE	TECHNOLOGY	ENGINEERING	ARTS	MATH	ELA
1-ESS1-1	ISTE.3.c		Creating #1		CCSS.ELA-LITERACY.W.1.3
			Creating #2		
			Creating #3		

SCIENCE & ENGINEERING PRACTICES

Analyzing and Interpreting Data: Use observations (firsthand or from media) to describe patterns in the natural world in order to answer scientific questions.

CROSSCUTTING CONCEPTS

Patterns: Patterns in the natural world can be observed, used to describe phenomena, and used as evidence.

TARGET VOCABULARY

constellation

star

Ursa Major (Big Dipper)

MATERIALS

- black construction paper (night sky)
- brass fasteners (stars)
- crayons (white to mark on the paper where to add the stars)
- pictures of the northern night sky that contain Ursa Major (the Big Dipper)

LITERACY CONNECTIONS

Our Stars
by Anne Rockwell

Zoo in the Sky: A Book About Animal Constellations
by Jacqueline Mitton

They Dance in the Sky: Native American Star Myths
by Jean Guard Monroe and Ray A. Williamson

NOTES

STEAM Design Challenges Gr. 1 © 2017 Creative Teaching Press

STEAM —IN— ACTION

DILEMMA ENGAGE

Allison the astronomer has been asked to create a star map for the astronomy museum. There are many, many stars in the sky, so she needs help. Allison has noticed that Polaris, the North Star, stays in about the same place in the sky all night and the other stars seem to move. Allison needs you to help find Polaris and then use that information to create a map of Ursa Major.

MISSION

Create a model of Ursa Major (the Big Dipper).

BLUEPRINT EXPLORE

Provide the Individual Blueprint Design sheet, and ask students to sketch three to four prototypes. Once drawings are complete, have each group decide which design to use to construct the prototype and fill out the Group Blueprint Design sheet. Before providing materials, have students write or verbalize why they chose to construct the prototype they selected and why they feel that the other designs would not work as well.

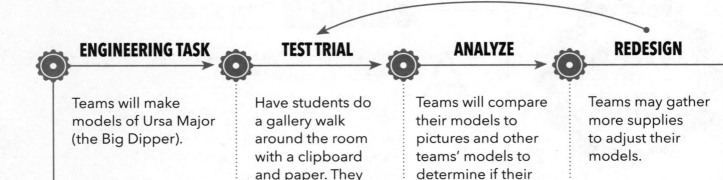

ENGINEERING TASK	**TEST TRIAL**	**ANALYZE**	**REDESIGN**
Teams will make models of Ursa Major (the Big Dipper).	Have students do a gallery walk around the room with a clipboard and paper. They can write down observations and comments.	Teams will compare their models to pictures and other teams' models to determine if their models accurately represent Ursa Major.	Teams may gather more supplies to adjust their models.

 HELPFUL TIPS

- After the Test Trial, have teams take a gallery walk to view other teams' designs for possible ideas to assist them in the Analyze and Redesign portions of the engineering design process.

- If teams are successful on the first try, encourage them to make their prototypes even more efficient. If it is a scenario in which this is not feasible, distribute team members to other teams to be a support for them in making their prototypes more efficient. Alternatively, at teacher discretion, move students on to the Justification portion of the lesson.

- If after the third test the final prototype is still unsuccessful, have students write how they would start over. These challenges are meant to have students build on what they originally designed. If the design proved to be unsuccessful, encourage a reflection/justification on what they would do if they were allowed to start again from scratch.

REFLECTIONS EXPLAIN & ELABORATE

AFTER TEST TRIAL 1	Did your model match the models of other teams?
	Did you accurately create a model of Ursa Major?
ANALYSIS	If your model did not match other models, review pictures of the night sky and check to see that you have the correct stars in your constellation. If there are mistakes, correct them.
AFTER TEST TRIAL 2	Did your model match other models?
ANALYSIS	If your model did not match other models, review pictures of the night sky and check to see that you have the correct stars in your constellation. If there are mistakes, correct them.
AFTER TEST TRIAL 3	Does your model match other models?
	Does it resemble Ursa Major?

JUSTIFICATION EVALUATE

ARTS

Draw a map of Ursa Minor.

TECHNOLOGY

Write a story about Ursa Major and Polaris, much like the Native Americans did.

Note: Teachers will want to read aloud Native American stories about constellations before assigning this activity.

AS TIME GOES BY

1-2 HOURS

TIME FOR COMPLETION

SETTING —THE— STAGE

DESIGN CHALLENGE PURPOSE

Construct a freestanding clock tower that has four sections on the clock face.

TEACHER DEVELOPMENT

This lesson is intended to be done after completing math units on telling time and partitioning shapes. In order for students to be able to complete this challenge, they will need to know that a circle can be partitioned into halves and quarters. Then relate that understanding to the structure of a clock face and how it can be partitioned into quarters (3 o'clock, 6 o'clock, 9 o'clock, and 12 o'clock). The lesson requires students to apply the steps of the engineering and STEAM design processes to complete the challenge. Refer to the STEAM design process diagram (page 15) for a description of each step.

STUDENT DEVELOPMENT

This is a great lesson for teaching the engineering process to students. Introduce the words **blueprint**, **design**, **engineer**, and **prototype** to your students. Teach them how to collaborate and work as a team. Use the STEAM job cards (page 143) to assign jobs to students to demonstrate the importance of working together.

STANDARDS

SCIENCE	TECHNOLOGY	ENGINEERING	ARTS	MATH	ELA
		K-2-ETS1-1	Creating #1	CCSS.MATH.CONTENT.1.MD.B.3	CCSS.ELA-LITERACY.W.1.1
		K-2-ETS1-2	Creating #2	CCSS.MATH.CONTENT.1.G.A.3	CCSS.ELA-LITERACY.SL.1.1
		K-2-ETS1-3	Creating #3		CCSS.ELA-LITERACY.L.1.2.D
					CCSS.ELA-LITERACY.L.1.5

SCIENCE & ENGINEERING PRACTICES

Asking Questions and Defining Problems: Define a simple problem that can be solved through the development of a new or improved object or tool.

Developing and Using Models: Develop a simple model based on evidence to represent a proposed object or tool.

Constructing Explanations and Designing Solutions: Use tools and/or materials to design and/or build a device that solves a specific problem or a solution to a specific problem.

CROSSCUTTING CONCEPTS

Structure and Function: The shape and stability of structures of natural and designed objects are related to their function.

TARGET VOCABULARY

clock

half hour

hour

time

tower

MATERIALS

- straws
- tape
- construction paper
- glue
- pipe cleaners
- craft sticks
- empty cereal boxes
- scissors

LITERACY CONNECTIONS

The Clock and the Mouse: A Teaching Rhyme About Time by Sandy Turley

Around the Clock by Roz Chast

NOTES

STEAM —IN— ACTION

DILEMMA　ENGAGE

Theo the timekeeper has the important job of taking care of the clock tower. He recently noticed that there is a crack in the clock face and the tower is shaky. Theo needs help coming up with a design for a new clock tower that is sturdy. He also needs to be able to take down one half hour of the clock face at a time in order to clean it. Help Theo by building a prototype of a clock tower with a clock face that can be removed.

MISSION

Build a clock tower that stands on its own. The clock face needs four sections that can be taken down without making the tower fall.

BLUEPRINT　EXPLORE

Provide the Individual Blueprint Design sheet, and ask students to sketch three to four prototypes. Once drawings are complete, have each group decide which design to use to construct the prototype and fill out the Group Blueprint Design sheet. Before providing materials, have students write or verbalize why they chose to construct the prototype they selected and why they feel that the other designs would not work as well.

ENGINEERING TASK   **TEST TRIAL**   **ANALYZE**   **REDESIGN**

ENGINEERING TASK	TEST TRIAL	ANALYZE	REDESIGN
Each team will design and construct a freestanding clock tower that has a face with removable sections.	Each team will build a freestanding clock tower and then attempt to remove one half hour worth of pieces from the clock face without making the structure fall.	Teams should be allowed to observe the other designs to gather ideas, reflect, and make changes in order to improve their prototypes.	Teams can use a colored pencil to make adjustments to their original design sketches. Teams will present the changes to the teacher for approval before making changes to the prototypes. Then they can get more supplies to rebuild and retest their prototypes.

HELPFUL TIPS

- After the Test Trial, have teams take a gallery walk to view other teams' designs for possible ideas to assist them in the Analyze and Redesign portions of the engineering design process.

- If teams are successful on the first try, encourage them to make their prototypes even more efficient. If it is a scenario in which this is not feasible, distribute team members to other teams to be a support for them in making their prototypes more efficient. Alternatively, at teacher discretion, move students on to the Justification portion of the lesson.

- If after the third test the final prototype is still unsuccessful, have students write how they would start over. These challenges are meant to have students build on what they originally designed. If the design proved to be unsuccessful, encourage a reflection/ justification on what they would do if they were allowed to start again from scratch.

REFLECTIONS — EXPLAIN & ELABORATE

AFTER TEST TRIAL 1	Did your tower stay standing when you took off a half hour worth of pieces from the clock face? Did the other pieces of the clock face remain on the tower?
ANALYSIS	What changes should you make to your prototype to make sure it meets the requirements?
AFTER TEST TRIAL 2	Did your tower stay standing when you took off a half hour worth of pieces from the clock face? What changes did you make that helped your prototype stay standing?
ANALYSIS	What changes still need to be made to your prototype?
AFTER TEST TRIAL 3	Was your prototype successful?

JUSTIFICATION — EVALUATE

ARTS	Draw a poster to advertise your clock tower design.
ELA	Write a rhyming phrase about your clock tower that Theo the Timekeeper can use at a town celebration for the new clock. Read *Around the Clock* by Roz Chast for ideas.

DEFLATED DEVELOPMENTS

STEAM

SETTING —THE— STAGE

DESIGN CHALLENGE PURPOSE

Build three different composite shapes from two-dimensional shapes.

TEACHER DEVELOPMENT

This activity challenges students to make composite shapes out of the listed two-dimensional shapes. **Composite shapes** are figures that are made of two or more other shapes. An example of a composite shape is when two right triangles are combined to make a square.

STUDENT DEVELOPMENT

First grade students need to understand certain two-dimensional shapes and how they are combined to create composite shapes. The shapes that students need to recognize for the math standard are rectangles, squares, trapezoids, triangles, half circles, and quarter circles.

Students need background knowledge on what a composite shape is and an understanding that some composite shapes make new plane shapes. For example, when two right triangles are combined to create a composite shape, the resulting shape is a square, and an equilateral triangle combined with a square makes a pentagon.

STANDARDS

SCIENCE	TECHNOLOGY	ENGINEERING	ARTS	MATH	ELA
	ISTE.3C	K-2-ETS1-1	Creating #1	CCSS.MATH. CONTENT.1.G.A.2	CCSS.ELA-LITERACY.SL.1.1
		K-2-ETS1-2	Creating #2		CCSS.ELA-LITERACY.W.1.1
		K-2-ETS1-3	Creating #3		CCSS.ELA-LITERACY.W.1.6

SCIENCE & ENGINEERING PRACTICES

Asking Questions and Defining Problems: Ask questions based on observations to find more information about the natural and/or designed world(s). Define a simple problem that can be solved through the development of a new or improved object or tool.

Developing and Using Models: Develop a simple model based on evidence to represent a proposed object or tool.

Analyzing and Interpreting Data: Analyze data from tests of an object or tool to determine if it works as intended.

CROSSCUTTING CONCEPTS

Structure and Function: The shape and stability of structures of natural and designed objects are related to their function(s).

TARGET VOCABULARY

composite shape

half circle

quarter circle

rectangle

square

trapezoid

triangle

MATERIALS

- paper cut into the following shapes: half circles, quarter circles, rectangles, squares, trapezoids, triangles
- stickers
- crayons
- markers
- building contract (page 132)

LITERACY CONNECTIONS

Flat Stanley: His Original Adventure
by Jeff Brown

Shape by Shape
by Suse MacDonald

NOTES

STEAM —IN— ACTION

DILEMMA ENGAGE

Samantha Skinny, Jane Plane, and Penny Pancake need to hire a builder. They are moving to Flat City, where everything is flat, including the houses! Samantha, Jane, and Penny need to hire a construction team to create one house for each of them. The houses must be made from composite shapes. The housing development does not allow the same exact shapes to be used together on the same house. The houses must also be decorated. The team that makes three different houses and follows the rules will win the building contract.

MISSION

Build houses for Samantha, Jane, and Penny.

Follow these rules:

1. The houses must be made by first combining plane shapes to create composite shapes. Then those composite shapes are combined to build the houses.
2. All three houses must use different composite shapes.
3. Each house should be decorated.

BLUEPRINT EXPLORE

Provide the Individual Blueprint Design sheet, and ask students to sketch three to four prototypes. Once drawings are complete, have each group decide which design to use to construct the prototype and fill out the Group Blueprint Design sheet. Before providing materials, have students write or verbalize why they chose to construct the prototype they selected and why they feel that the other designs would not work as well.

ENGINEERING TASK	**TEST TRIAL**	**ANALYZE**	**REDESIGN**
Each team will build three different houses by combining plane shapes to make composite shapes.	Teams will probably do more testing for this challenge on their blueprint design sheets, figuring out what composite shapes are created by combining two or more shapes. The teacher will review teams' work. After review, teams may want to adjust or change some shapes in order to improve their designs.	When reviewing their new "houses," have the students ask themselves whether they followed the rules of the challenge. Teams should be allowed to observe the other designs to gather ideas, reflect, and make changes in order to improve their prototypes.	After reviewing their designs to make sure they followed the rules of the challenge, teams will make adjustments to their designs. Then they can get new supplies to rebuild and retest their prototypes.

HELPFUL TIPS

- After the Test Trial, have teams take a gallery walk to view other teams' designs for possible ideas to assist them in the Analyze and Redesign portions of the engineering design process.

- If teams are successful on the first try, encourage them to make their prototypes even more efficient. If it is a scenario in which this is not feasible, distribute team members to other teams to be a support for them in making their prototypes more efficient. Alternatively, at teacher discretion, move students on to the Justification portion of the lesson.

- If after the third test the final prototype is still unsuccessful, have students write how they would start over. These challenges are meant to have students build on what they originally designed. If the design proved to be unsuccessful, encourage a reflection/ justification on what they would do if they were allowed to start again from scratch.

REFLECTIONS EXPLAIN & ELABORATE

AFTER TEST TRIAL 1	Were you able to combine plane shapes to make a composite shape (house)? Did you make three different composite shape houses?
ANALYSIS	Do your composite shapes look like plane shapes? If not, what will you change?
AFTER TEST TRIAL 2	Did you combine shapes to make composite shapes? Do all three of the houses look different from each other?
ANALYSIS	Were you able to adjust your shapes to meet all of the building requirements? Do you need to make any adjustments? Are the houses decorated?
AFTER TEST TRIAL 3	Did your team meet the requirements of the challenge?

JUSTIFICATION EVALUATE

ARTS	Create a sign that advertises the designs of your three houses.
ELA	Write a letter to your family describing the houses you built.
TECHNOLOGY	Use Word or Publisher to create a poster advertising your houses.

GEO WORLD

STEAM

SETTING —THE— STAGE

DESIGN CHALLENGE PURPOSE

Create an area of the World's Fair dedicated to a specific three-dimensional shape.

TEACHER DEVELOPMENT

The World's Fair is an opportunity for countries to show off technological innovations and accomplishments. For example, the electric lightbulb debuted at the 1893 World's Fair. The World's Fair exhibition happens every year or two all around the world. Cities that are interested in hosting the fair need to explain why their city should be chosen. The cities send in their plans and a small model to help the fair committee make its decision. Discuss with students how a city might prepare to submit a model.

Houston, Texas, and San Francisco, California, are among the cities that are bidding for the chance to host the fair in 2025. Encourage your students to imagine what they think futuristic buildings will look like in the year 2025.

Note: You can calculate your students' ages and tell them how old they will be in the year 2025.

Note: Visit the website listed on the inside front cover for more information about the World's Fair.

STUDENT DEVELOPMENT

Students will need to understand how composite shapes are created from two-dimensional shapes before trying to create three-dimensional composite shapes. They will need to understand what a World's Fair is. Show them pictures or videos of past fairs; pictures of modern art sculptures made from composite shapes; and futuristic buildings to help them get ideas for the challenge.

Lesson Ideas: Lead a discussion about the different three-dimensional shapes that students will encounter during this challenge.

Give students three-dimensional blocks to play with in order to try to create composite shapes. Have students assemble their three-dimensional shapes in preparation for this lesson using the three-dimensional templates (page 132-135).

STANDARDS

SCIENCE	TECHNOLOGY	ENGINEERING	ARTS	MATH	ELA
		K-2-ETS1-1	Creating #1	CCSS.MATH.CONTENT.1.G.2	CCSS.ELA-LITERACY.W.1.3,
		K-2-ETS1-2	Creating #2		CCSS.ELA-LITERACY.SL.1.1
		K-2-ETS1-3	Creating #3		

SCIENCE & ENGINEERING PRACTICES

Constructing Explanations and Designing Solutions: Make observations (firsthand or from media) to construct an evidence-based account for natural phenomena.

CROSSCUTTING CONCEPTS

Energy and Matter: Objects may break into smaller pieces and be put together into larger pieces, or change shapes.

TARGET VOCABULARY

cone

cube

cylinder

rectangular prism

MATERIALS

- tape
- scissors
- multiple copies of three-dimensional paper shapes (page 133-136)

Note:

- Print the 3-D shapes onto heavy cardstock for durability.
- Have parent volunteers assemble the 3-D shapes ahead of time or use 3-D shape blocks or foam shapes instead of printing the shapes onto paper.

LITERACY CONNECTIONS

Night of the New Magicians
by Mary Pope Osborne

Mr. Ferris and His Wheel
by Kathryn Gibbs Davis

Captain Invincible and the Space Shapes
by Stuart J. Murphy

NOTES

DILEMMA ENGAGE

The mayor of Houston, Texas, needs help! His city wants to host the 2025 World's Fair. The city needs to send its theme idea and model to the fair committee. The mayor's theme idea is to build a Geo World. This futuristic world would have different areas with buildings and landscaping made from a different three-dimensional composite shape. There will be an area made from cubes, one made from rectangular prisms, one made from cones, and one made from cylinders. Help the mayor design an area of the fair for his Geo World model.

MISSION

Build an area of Geo World with a building and bushes or trees made from composite shapes.

Follow these rules:

1. Make a blueprint of your building and plants. Then label the composite shapes you used.

2. Use the assigned three-dimensional shape to make a composite shape building and bushes or trees.

3. Give your area a name.

BLUEPRINT EXPLORE

Provide the Individual Blueprint Design sheet, and ask students to sketch three to four prototypes. Once drawings are complete, have each group decide which design to use to construct the prototype and fill out the Group Blueprint Design sheet. Before providing materials, have students write or verbalize why they chose to construct the prototype they selected and why they feel that the other designs would not work as well.

ENGINEERING TASK	TEST TRIAL	ANALYZE	REDESIGN
Each team will use three-dimensional shapes made of paper to create composite shapes and then use those shapes to construct a building and bushes or trees. *Note:* Assign each team a different three-dimensional shape to use when designing its building, bushes, or trees.	Teams will probably do more testing for this challenge on their blueprints, figuring out what composite shapes are made by combining two shapes. The teacher should review students' work. After review, students may want to change or adjust the shapes to improve their designs.	When reviewing their building and plants, have the teams ask themselves whether they met the requirements of this challenge. Teams should be allowed to observe the other designs to gather ideas, reflect, and make changes in order to improve their prototypes.	Teams need to review their blueprints and compare them to their three-dimensional designs to see if they match. They need to review their composite shapes to determine if the composite shapes all use the assigned shape.

HELPFUL TIPS

- After the Test Trial, have teams take a gallery walk to view other teams' designs for possible ideas to assist them in the Analyze and Redesign portions of the engineering design process.

- If teams are successful on the first try, encourage them to make their prototypes even more efficient. If it is a scenario in which this is not feasible, distribute team members to other teams to be a support for them in making their prototypes more efficient. Alternatively, at teacher discretion, move students on to the Justification portion of the lesson.

- If after the third test the final prototype is still unsuccessful, have students write how they would start over. These challenges are meant to have students build on what they originally designed. If the design proved to be unsuccessful, encourage a reflection/ justification on what they would do if they were allowed to start again from scratch.

REFLECTIONS — EXPLAIN & ELABORATE

AFTER TEST TRIAL 1	Are your building and plants made of three-dimensional composite shapes? Is your assigned three-dimensional shape in all of your composite shapes? Do you have a unique name for your area?
ANALYSIS	What changes should you make to improve your design so that it meets all of the requirements?
AFTER TEST TRIAL 2	Is your assigned shape used in all of your composite shapes? Does your model match your blueprint?
ANALYSIS	Which composite shapes do you need to change so that you meet the requirements? What changes do you need to make to help your model match your blueprint?
AFTER TEST TRIAL 3	Did you meet all of the requirements?

JUSTIFICATION — EVALUATE

ARTS	Create a poster about your model for part of Geo World. Draw a picture of the building you created, showing the composite shapes that you used.
ELA	Write the steps you took to create your building.

TO GET TO THE OTHER SIDE

s t E A m

SETTING —THE— STAGE

DESIGN CHALLENGE PURPOSE

Build a bridge that supports a textbook.

TEACHER DEVELOPMENT

This lesson is meant to introduce students to the engineering and STEAM design processes. Students will explore the process by designing and building a prototype, testing it, and then making changes to meet the requirements of the challenge. Refer to the STEAM design process diagram (page 15) for an explanation of each step.

Note: Visit the website listed on the inside front cover for helpful hints to guide teams as they construct their bridges.

STUDENT DEVELOPMENT

This is a great lesson for teaching the engineering design process to students. Introduce the words **blueprint**, **design**, **engineer**, and **prototype** to your students. Teach them how to collaborate and work as a team. Use the STEAM job cards (page 143) to assign jobs to students to make the process easier to manage and to show the importance of working together.

STANDARDS

SCIENCE	TECHNOLOGY	ENGINEERING	ARTS	MATH	ELA
		K-2-ETS1-1	Creating #1		CCSS.ELA-LITERACY.W.1.1
		K-2-ETS1-2	Creating #2		CCSS.ELA-LITERACY.SL.1.1
		K-2-ETS1-3	Creating #3		

SCIENCE & ENGINEERING PRACTICES

Asking Questions and Defining Problems: Define a simple problem that can be solved through the development of a new or improved object or tool.

Developing and Using Models: Develop a simple model based on evidence to represent a proposed object or tool.

Constructing Explanations and Designing Solutions: Use tools and/or materials to design and/or build a device that solves a specific problem or a solution to a specific problem.

CROSSCUTTING CONCEPTS

Structure and Function: The shape and stability of structures of natural and designed objects are related to their function.

TARGET VOCABULARY

blueprint

design

engineer

prototype

structure

weight

MATERIALS

- textbook (each team will use the same book)
- 2 sheets of paper
- 12 in. of tape
- scissors
- ruler

LITERACY CONNECTIONS

The Little Red Lighthouse and the Great Gray Bridge by Hildegarde H. Swift

NOTES

STEAM IN ACTION

DILEMMA | ENGAGE

The small town of Bridgeville needs a new bridge built across the river. The mayor of Bridgeville is looking for an engineering team to build a bridge prototype. Can you build a model of a bridge to help the mayor?

MISSION

Build a bridge prototype.

Follow these rules:

1. You may only use the materials provided.

2. The bridge must hold the weight of a textbook.

3. The bridge must hold the textbook for one minute without being crushed.

BLUEPRINT | EXPLORE

Provide the Individual Blueprint Design sheet, and ask students to sketch three to four prototypes. Once drawings are complete, have each group decide which design to use to construct the prototype and fill out the Group Blueprint Design sheet. Before providing materials, have students write or verbalize why they chose to construct the prototype they selected and why they feel that the other designs would not work as well.

ENGINEERING TASK   **TEST TRIAL**   **ANALYZE**   **REDESIGN**

ENGINEERING TASK	TEST TRIAL	ANALYZE	REDESIGN
Each team will construct a bridge prototype. *Note:* Successful bridges will likely be constructed by cutting the paper into four pieces and then rolling those pieces into cylinders to serve as the bridge supports.	Each team will place a textbook on its bridge to see if it can hold a book for one minute.	Teams should be allowed to observe the other designs to gather ideas, reflect, and make changes in order to improve their prototypes.	Teams can use a colored pencil to make adjustments to their original design sketches. Teams will present the changes to the teacher for approval before making changes to the prototypes. Then they can get new supplies to rebuild and retest their prototypes.

 HELPFUL TIPS

- After the Test Trial, have teams take a gallery walk to view other teams' designs for possible ideas to assist them in the Analyze and Redesign portions of the engineering design process.

- If teams are successful on the first try, encourage them to make their prototypes even more efficient. If it is a scenario in which this is not feasible, distribute team members to other teams to be a support for them in making their prototypes more efficient. Alternatively, at teacher discretion, move students on to the Justification portion of the lesson.

- If after the third test the final prototype is still unsuccessful, have students write how they would start over. These challenges are meant to have students build on what they originally designed. If the design proved to be unsuccessful, encourage a reflection/justification on what they would do if they were allowed to start again from scratch.

REFLECTIONS — EXPLAIN & ELABORATE

AFTER TEST TRIAL 1	How long did your bridge prototype hold the book? Which team of engineers had a bridge that held the book for one minute?
ANALYSIS	What were some of the differences between the bridge prototypes? What changes will you make to your bridge?
AFTER TEST TRIAL 2	Did your bridge hold the textbook longer this time?
ANALYSIS	What changes did other teams make to build a stronger bridge? What changes will you make to strengthen your bridge?
AFTER TEST TRIAL 3	Did your bridge hold the textbook for one minute? If you could start again, what would you do differently?

JUSTIFICATION — EVALUATE

ARTS	Create a poster advertising your bridge.
ELA	Write a letter to the mayor of Bridgeville explaining why your bridge prototype should be the winning structure.

TREMENDOUS TOWERS

1-2 HOURS

TIME FOR COMPLETION

SETTING
— THE —
STAGE

DESIGN CHALLENGE PURPOSE

Design the tallest freestanding tower.

TEACHER DEVELOPMENT

This is an engineering challenge. It is important to understand the steps involved in the engineering and STEAM design processes. Refer to the STEAM design process diagram (page 15) for a description of each step. The mathematical concepts involved in this lesson are derived from first grade measurement standards.

STUDENT DEVELOPMENT

This is a great lesson for teaching the engineering process to students. Introduce the words **blueprint**, **design**, **engineer**, and **prototype** to your students. Teach them how to collaborate and work as a team. Use the STEAM job cards (page 143) to assign jobs to students to make the process easier to manage and to teach the importance of working together.

STANDARDS

SCIENCE	TECHNOLOGY	ENGINEERING	ARTS	MATH	ELA
	ISTE.3	K-2-ETS1-1	Creating #1	CCSS.MATH. CONTENT.1.MD.A.1	CCSS.ELA- LITERACY.SL.1.1
		K-2-ETS1-2	Creating #2	CCSS.MATH. CONTENT.1.MD.A.2	
		K-2-ETS1-3	Creating #3		
			Performing/ Presenting/ Producing #4, #5, #6		

SCIENCE & ENGINEERING PRACTICES

Asking Questions and Defining Problems: Ask questions based on observations to find more information about the natural and/or designed world. Define a simple problem that can be solved through the development of a new or improved object or tool.

Developing and Using Models: Develop a simple model based on evidence to represent a proposed object or tool.

Analyzing and Interpreting Data: Analyze data from tests of an object or tool to determine if it works as intended.

CROSSCUTTING CONCEPTS

Structure and Function: The shape and stability of structures of natural and designed objects are related to their function(s).

TARGET VOCABULARY

blueprint
design
engineer
prototype

MATERIALS

- 15 pipe cleaners
- 12 in. of masking tape
- building contract (page 137)

Note: Use yarn or paper clips to measure the tower.

LITERACY CONNECTIONS

Pop-up New York
by Andy Mansfield

How Big Is a Foot?
by Rolf Myller

NOTES

DILEMMA | ENGAGE

Mayor B. Tall of the town of Tinyville wants to build a skyscraper that towers above the rest of the buildings in town. Tourism is down, and he needs to make the citizens of Tinyville feel great about their town again. Help him build a prototype of the tower. The team with the tallest freestanding tower will win a building contract and get to name the tower.

MISSION

Build the tallest freestanding tower possible.

BLUEPRINT | EXPLORE

Provide the Individual Blueprint Design sheet, and ask students to sketch three to four prototypes. Once drawings are complete, have each group decide which design to use to construct the prototype and fill out the Group Blueprint Design sheet. Before providing materials, have students write or verbalize why they chose to construct the prototype they selected and why they feel that the other designs would not work as well.

ENGINEERING TASK **TEST TRIAL** **ANALYZE** **REDESIGN**

ENGINEERING TASK	TEST TRIAL	ANALYZE	REDESIGN
Teams construct their towers. *Note:* As an extension or to determine the winner in the case of a tie, place a large marshmallow at the top of the tower. Keep adding marshmallows until a tower falls and a winner is decided.	Teams will measure and record the height of their towers and then make observations about their sturdiness.	Teams should be allowed to observe the other designs to gather ideas, reflect, and make changes in order to improve their prototypes.	Teams can use a colored pencil to make adjustments to their original design sketches. Teams will present the changes to the teacher for approval before making changes to the prototypes. Then they can get new supplies to rebuild and retest their prototypes.

HELPFUL TIPS

- After the Test Trial, have teams take a gallery walk to view other teams' designs for possible ideas to assist them in the Analyze and Redesign portions of the engineering design process.

- If teams are successful on the first try, encourage them to make their prototypes even more efficient. If it is a scenario in which this is not feasible, distribute team members to other teams to be a support for them in making their prototypes more efficient. Alternatively, at teacher discretion, move students on to the Justification portion of the lesson.

- If after the third test the final prototype is still unsuccessful, have students write how they would start over. These challenges are meant to have students build on what they originally designed. If the design proved to be unsuccessful, encourage a reflection/ justification on what they would do if they were allowed to start again from scratch.

REFLECTIONS — EXPLAIN & ELABORATE

AFTER TEST TRIAL 1	Which team had the tallest tower? What was the height of your tower?
ANALYSIS	Did everyone come up with the same design? What designs seem to work best?
AFTER TEST TRIAL 2	Was you tower taller this time? What was the height of your tower compared to the height of other teams' towers?
ANALYSIS	Why do you think the tallest tower was able to stand on its own? What changes could you make to your design to make your tower taller and more stable?
AFTER TEST TRIAL 3	Was your final tower taller than in your first two trials? What was the difference between the tallest tower and the shortest tower?

JUSTIFICATION — EVALUATE

ARTS	Design a billboard prototype to present at the Tinyville town council meeting advertising your tower. Present the billboard to an audience.
ARTS/ TECHNOLOGY	Record a commercial for your new tower.

AIR BOWLING

S T E A m

SETTING —THE— STAGE

DESIGN CHALLENGE PURPOSE

Create an adaptation for your body so that you can knock over cardboard air bowling pins.

TEACHER DEVELOPMENT

Adaptations are unique for different animal species. **Adaptations** are the different features or characteristics that plants or animals have that allow them to survive in their particular environment. Adaptations can be either physical or behavioral. An example of a physical adaptation is a bird's beak. For example, a pelican has a large bill with a stretchable pouch on the bottom. This adaptation allows the pelican to catch fish underwater. An example of behavioral adaptation is hibernation. The black bear will hibernate during the cold months of winter. Be sure to mention birds during your discussion. Include information about how birds' wings help them fly and some birds' webbed feet help them move in water.

Students will need to understand that animals live in certain habitats and eat certain food. Young students sometimes have a hard time understanding that animals cannot simply move to a new habitat or change what they eat. It is important when introducing this challenge to also talk about camouflage and how animals use this adaptation to survive.

Note: Visit the website listed on the inside front cover for information about animal adaptations.

STEAM

STUDENT DEVELOPMENT

Students will need background knowledge on different adaptations that animals possess to assist them in accomplishing tasks. Some animals are the same color as the area that they live in or have patterns on their bodies that help them to blend in with their surroundings. This helps to protect them from other animals that may want to eat them. Animals can also have body parts that help them survive. Some animals have webbed feet that help them swim, some have claws to help grip things or rip their food apart, and some have fur to keep them warm. Think of some more animal body parts that help animals survive. One adaptation that you think of should be able to create wind and will help you with the challenge.

Teacher Hint: Show several pictures of animals and point out the different adaptations that help them survive. Be sure to include pictures of webbed feet and wings. Students will also need to know about the sport of bowling.

Note: Visit the website listed on the inside front cover for more information about animal adaptations.

STANDARDS

SCIENCE	TECHNOLOGY	ENGINEERING	ARTS	MATH	ELA
1- LS1-1	ISTE.3	K-2-ETS1-1	Creating #1		CCSS.ELA-LITERACY.W.1
		K-2-ETS1-2	Creating #2		
		K-2-ETS1-3	Creating #3		

SCIENCE & ENGINEERING PRACTICES

Constructing and Designing Solutions: Use tools and/or materials to design and/or build a device that solves a specific problem or a solution to a specific problem.

CROSSCUTTING CONCEPTS

Structure and Function: The shape and stability of structures of natural and designed objects are related to their function(s).

TARGET VOCABULARY

adapt

adaptation

MATERIALS

- 10 paper towel tubes
- construction paper for making adaptations
- tape
- scissors
- animal adaptations cards (page 138)

LITERACY CONNECTIONS

I Wish I Had Duck Feet by Dr. Seuss

NOTES

STEAM IN ACTION

DILEMMA ENGAGE

Bobby owns a bowling alley, but he has a problem. Bowling is not as popular as it used to be. To get people excited about bowling, Bobby invented a new version called air bowling. Instead of rolling a ball, players have to figure out how to adapt and move their bodies to knock over lightweight cardboard pins. Just like animals use their adaptations to do things, players must adapt their bodies to knock down the pins without touching them. Bobby needs you to help him test his new game.

MISSION

Make an adaptation for your body that resembles an animal adaptation. Use it to help you knock over the cardboard pins without touching them.

You must be able to explain what animal your adaptation came from and how the animal uses it to survive.

BLUEPRINT EXPLORE

Provide the Individual Blueprint Design sheet, and ask students to sketch three to four prototypes. Once drawings are complete, have each group decide which design to use to construct the prototype and fill out the Group Blueprint Design sheet. Before providing materials, have students write or verbalize why they chose to construct the prototype they selected and why they feel that the other designs would not work as well.

ENGINEERING TASK	TEST TRIAL	ANALYZE	REDESIGN
Each team will create an adaptation for a body part that mimics an animal adaptation. The team will use the adaptation to help its members play air bowling.	Team members will take turns testing the prototype by standing behind the designated line and attempting to knock over the cardboard pins using their adapted body part. *Note:* Place the line far enough away so that students have a difficult time trying to knock down the pins, but it should not be impossible. You do not want students to knock the pins all down on the first try.	Teams should be allowed to observe the other designs to gather ideas, reflect, and make changes in order to improve their prototypes. Teams can review pictures of animal adaptations to help direct their thinking as they evaluate their prototypes.	Teams can use a colored pencil to make adjustments to their original design sketches. Teams will present the changes to the teacher for approval before making changes to the prototypes. Then they can get new supplies to rebuild and retest their prototypes.

HELPFUL TIPS

- After the Test Trial, have teams take a gallery walk to view other teams' designs for possible ideas to assist them in the Analyze and Redesign portions of the engineering design process.

- If teams are successful on the first try, encourage them to make their prototypes even more efficient. If it is a scenario in which this is not feasible, distribute team members to other teams to be a support for them in making their prototypes more efficient. Alternatively, at teacher discretion, move students on to the Justification portion of the lesson.

- If after the third test the final prototype is still unsuccessful, have students write how they would start over. These challenges are meant to have students build on what they originally designed. If the design proved to be unsuccessful, encourage a reflection/justification on what they would do if they were allowed to start again from scratch.

REFLECTIONS — EXPLAIN & ELABORATE

AFTER TEST TRIAL 1	Which animal adaptation did you mimic, or copy? Were you successful at knocking down the pins? How many pins did you knock down?
ANALYSIS	Are you going to adjust your adaptation or choose a different animal adaptation? Explain.
AFTER TEST TRIAL 2	Were you successful at knocking down the pins? What animal adaptation did you mimic, or copy?
ANALYSIS	Are you going to adjust your adaptation or choose a different animal adaptation? Explain.
AFTER TEST TRIAL 3	Was your final animal adaptation successful? Which animal adaptations were most successful at knocking down the pins? Explain.

JUSTIFICATION — EVALUATE

TECHNOLOGY	Use Junior Safe Search to research one of the four animals from the challenge to find out more about their habitat, what they eat, and an adaptation that helps them survive.
ARTS	Animals also use camouflage as an adaptation. Review information about the adaptation that you chose and which animals use it. Then, after determining the animal, research the animal's habitat and add color or texture to your design in order help camouflage the animal in its habitat.
ELA	Review information about the adaptation that you chose and which animals use it. Write some facts that you found in your research.

BEARS BUILD BARRIERS

S t E A M

SETTING —THE— STAGE

DESIGN CHALLENGE PURPOSE

Build a prototype that mimics a plant's external parts.

TEACHER DEVELOPMENT

Plants use their **external parts** (e.g., roots, stem, and leaves) to survive, grow, and meet their needs. In this challenge, students are asked to think about how plants use their external parts to protect themselves as they design a prototype to keep intruders out of the Bear family's home.

BEARS BUILD BARRIERS

STUDENT DEVELOPMENT

Ensure students are familiar with the vocabulary terms related to the challenge. Students should review the protective parts of different types of plants, such as cactus spines and rose thorns.

Lesson Idea: Bring in several plants for students to examine. Be sure to include one that has either thorns or spines. Gently take the plants out of their pot, and lay them out on newspaper. Have students examine them for similarities and differences. Make a class chart listing what they observe. Discuss the function of the different plant parts.

STANDARDS

SCIENCE	TECHNOLOGY	ENGINEERING	ARTS	MATH	ELA
1-LS1-1		K-2-ETS1-1	Creating #1	CCSS.MATH. CONTENT.1.MD.C.4	CCSS.ELA-LITERACY.SL.1.4
		K-2-ETS1-2	Creating #2		
		K-2-ETS1-3	Creating #3		

SCIENCE & ENGINEERING PRACTICES

Constructing Explanations and Designing Solutions: Make observations (firsthand or from media) to construct an evidence-based account for natural phenomena. Use tools and/or materials to design and/or build a device that solves a specific problem or a solution to a specific problem.

CROSSCUTTING CONCEPTS

Structure and Function: The shape and stability of structures of natural and designed objects are related to their function(s).

TARGET VOCABULARY

external

intruder

mimic

spine (cactus)

structure

thorn

MATERIALS

Barrier:

- 10 toothpicks
- 2 pipe cleaners
- 1 sheet tissue paper
- 1 sheet construction paper
- 10 twist ties
- 2 craft sticks
- 3 rubber bands
- tape
- scissors

Testing:

- 1 empty milk carton (represents the three bears' house)
- 1 1½ in. ball of clay (represents an intruder)

LITERACY CONNECTIONS

Goldilocks and the Three Bears
by James Marshall

NOTES

STEAM
—IN—
ACTION

DILEMMA **ENGAGE**

Baby bear is sad. A girl broke into his house and ate all his porridge, broke his favorite chair, and messed up his bed. Papa bear promised to build a barrier around the house to protect it from intruders, but Mama bear is worried that the barrier will look ugly and unfriendly to their visiting friends. Papa bear needs you to help him build a barrier that will protect their house and also look nice.

MISSION

Create a barrier that will protect the Bears' house. It must be decorated with at least five flowers and must mimic a plant part used for protection.

BLUEPRINT **EXPLORE**

Provide the Individual Blueprint Design sheet, and ask students to sketch three to four prototypes. Once drawings are complete, have each group decide which design to use to construct the prototype and fill out the Group Blueprint Design sheet. Before providing materials, have students write or verbalize why they chose to construct the prototype they selected and why they feel that the other designs would not work as well.

ENGINEERING TASK

Each team will build a barrier that mimics the protective parts of a plant's exterior in order to keep the three bears' house safe from uninvited guests.

TEST TRIAL

Gently roll the clay ball toward the barrier. If the ball is stopped by the barrier and does not touch the house, it is successful. If the barrier does not keep the ball from hitting the house, the team will need to redesign its prototype.

Note: Teachers may choose to roll the ball of clay or allow teams to release the clay ball from the top of a ramp toward the barrier to provide a more consistent amount of force during testing.

ANALYZE

Teams should be allowed to observe the other designs to gather ideas, reflect, and make changes in order to improve their prototypes.

REDESIGN

Teams can use a colored pencil to make adjustments to their original design sketches. Teams will present the changes to the teacher for approval before making changes to the prototypes. Then they can get new supplies to rebuild and retest their prototypes.

HELPFUL TIPS

- After the Test Trial, have teams take a gallery walk to view other teams' designs for possible ideas to assist them in the Analyze and Redesign portions of the engineering design process.

- If teams are successful on the first try, encourage them to make their prototypes even more efficient. If it is a scenario in which this is not feasible, distribute team members to other teams to be a support for them in making their prototypes more efficient. Alternatively, at teacher discretion, move students on to the Justification portion of the lesson.

- If after the third test the final prototype is still unsuccessful, have students write how they would start over. These challenges are meant to have students build on what they originally designed. If the design proved to be unsuccessful, encourage a reflection/ justification on what they would do if they were allowed to start again from scratch.

REFLECTIONS   EXPLAIN & ELABORATE

AFTER TEST TRIAL 1	Did your barrier prototype keep out the "intruder"? Explain. What materials did successful teams use to create their barriers?
ANALYSIS	How will you change your barrier prototype to make it more effective at keeping out the intruder?
AFTER TEST TRIAL 2	Did your barrier prototype keep out the "intruder"? Explain. What were the similarities and differences between the different teams' prototypes?
ANALYSIS	How will you change your barrier prototype to make it more effective at keeping out the "intruder"?
AFTER TEST TRIAL 3	Was your barrier successful at stopping the "intruder"? Explain. Discuss how your barrier is similar to real-world barriers that are used around homes.

JUSTIFICATION   EVALUATE

ARTS	Use construction paper and toilet paper tubes to create a forest of trees around the three bears' house. Put all of the teams' houses and forests together to create a class village. Include all of the barriers constructed during the challenge in the village display.
ELA	As a class, write an alternative version of "Goldilocks and the Three Bears" that includes Papa building a barrier to protect his house. The teacher will call on students to ask for suggestions to add to the class story.
MATH	Work with another student to create a bar graph of the different types of plant parts that are represented by the different barriers. Then find the difference between the different numbers of the plant parts used. *Note:* There will probably be only two different plant parts represented (e.g., cactus spines and rose thorns).

CAN IT STAND ALONE?

S·t·E·A·m

1-2 HOURS

TIME FOR COMPLETION

SETTING —THE— STAGE

DESIGN CHALLENGE PURPOSE

Create a freestanding model of a basketball hoop.

TEACHER DEVELOPMENT

Many animals use their tails to give themselves **stability** as they run, climb, swim, and do other things. Animals also use their tails to express feelings, such as fear. They can also use their tails as a weapon to protect themselves. Snakes, squirrels, and domestic cats sometimes use their tails to balance as they stand or reach up. Plants also have parts that help them stand up, such as a flower's stem.

In this challenge, students will design a solution to a human problem by **mimicking** how plants or animals use their external parts to help them survive.

Note: Visit the website listed on the inside front cover for information about how animals use their tails.

S t E A m

STUDENT DEVELOPMENT

Provide background information to students prior to the challenge about how animals use their tails to provide stability for themselves. This will help students with ideas for their designs. Animals use their tails to help them balance when they sit, stand on their back legs, or walk along tree branches. Their tails also help them swat flies, climb, and even grasp objects. The tail acts as an extra leg for support just as a tripod supports a camera or a telescope. Plants also have external parts that support the plant to make it stand up.

Note: Visit the website listed on the inside front cover for more information about how animals use their tails.

STANDARDS

SCIENCE	TECHNOLOGY	ENGINEERING	ARTS	MATH	ELA
1-LS1-1		K-2-ETS1-1	Creating #1		CCSS.ELA-LITERACY.SL.1.1.B
		K-2-ETS1-2	Creating #2		
		K-2-ETS1-3	Creating #3		

SCIENCE & ENGINEERING PRACTICES

Constructing Explanations and Designing Solutions: Use tools and/or materials to design and/or build a device that solves a specific problem or a solution to a specific problem.

CROSSCUTTING CONCEPTS

Structure and Function: The shape and stability of structures of natural and designed objects are related to their function(s).

Influence of Science, Engineering, and Technology on Society and the Natural World: Every human-made product is designed by applying some knowledge of the natural world and is built using materials derived from the natural world.

TARGET VOCABULARY

mimicking (mimic)

stability (stable)

MATERIALS

- straws
- tape
- pipe cleaner
- paper
- scissors
- basketball certificate (page 139)

LITERACY CONNECTIONS

Salt in His Shoes: Michael Jordan in Pursuit of a Dream by Deloris Jordan and Roslyn M. Jordan

The Everything Kids' Basketball Book by Bob Schaller with Coach Dave Harnish

What Do You Do with a Tail Like This? by Steve Jenkins and Robin Page

NOTES

STEAM —IN— ACTION

DILEMMA | ENGAGE

The students at Full Court Elementary School want to play basketball, but the playground does not have room for a basketball court. The students asked the principal if he could build the court in the corner of the school parking lot, but there is nowhere to hang the hoop. The principal agreed to put the basketball court in the corner of the parking lot as long as the students design a stand for the hoop. The students need your help!

Use what you know about how animals use their tails for stability to help the students design a stand for the basketball hoop. Teams that design hoops that stand on their own will receive a certificate of appreciation.

MISSION

Create a model of a basketball hoop that can stand on its own without being taped down to a surface. Then make a successful shot through the hoop.

BLUEPRINT | EXPLORE

Provide the Individual Blueprint Design sheet, and ask students to sketch three to four prototypes. Once drawings are complete, have each group decide which design to use to construct the prototype and fill out the Group Blueprint Design sheet. Before providing materials, have students write or verbalize why they chose to construct the prototype they selected and why they feel that the other designs would not work as well.

ENGINEERING TASK	TEST TRIAL	ANALYZE	REDESIGN
Each team will design a freestanding basketball hoop.	Each team will try tossing a paper ball through its hoop to test the stability of the basketball stand.	Teams should be allowed to observe the other designs to gather ideas, reflect, and make changes in order to improve their prototypes.	Teams can use a colored pencil to make adjustments to their original design sketches. Teams will present the changes to the teacher for approval before making changes to the prototypes. Then they can get new supplies to rebuild and retest their prototypes.

  # HELPFUL TIPS

- After the Test Trial, have teams take a gallery walk to view other teams' designs for possible ideas to assist them in the Analyze and Redesign portions of the engineering design process.

- If teams are successful on the first try, encourage them to make their prototypes even more efficient. If it is a scenario in which this is not feasible, distribute team members to other teams to be a support for them in making their prototypes more efficient. Alternatively, at teacher discretion, move students on to the Justification portion of the lesson.

- If after the third test the final prototype is still unsuccessful, have students write how they would start over. These challenges are meant to have students build on what they originally designed. If the design proved to be unsuccessful, encourage a reflection/justification on what they would do if they were allowed to start again from scratch.

REFLECTIONS — EXPLAIN & ELABORATE

AFTER TEST TRIAL 1	Did your model stay standing when you made a basket?
ANALYSIS	What changes can you make to your design to make it more stable? Can you think of the part of a plant that helps it stand up?
AFTER TEST TRIAL 2	Did your redesigned hoop stand on its own? Did it stay standing when you made a shot through the hoop?
ANALYSIS	Were your improvements helpful? What changes helped your model? What other adjustments can you make to your model?
AFTER TEST TRIAL 3	Was your team successful?

JUSTIFICATION — EVALUATE

ARTS	Design a blueprint of the entire basketball court at Full Court Elementary School.
ELA	Work with your team to give a short presentation about your model. Explain why it would be a good choice for Full Court Elementary School.

MUST FIND MY MAMA!

S T E A m

2 HOURS

TIME FOR COMPLETION

SETTING —THE— STAGE

DESIGN CHALLENGE PURPOSE

Build a device that allows students to see up and over an obstruction in order to match adult animals with their offspring.

TEACHER DEVELOPMENT

Animal offspring share the same **physical traits** (features) of their adult parents. For example, a mother zebra and her baby both have stripes and the same shaped head but are just different sizes.

The science standard addressed in this challenge focuses on comparing features to identify **offspring** (an animal's young). While the engineering challenge is to build a viewer, students will be meeting the science standard when they complete their mission.

STUDENT DEVELOPMENT

Students will build on their knowledge of **reflection** to use mirrors when creating their viewer prototype. Students must have the background knowledge that animal **offspring** look similar to their **parents** but not exactly alike.

Lesson Idea: Take students on a virtual field trip by visiting to your local zoo's website. Compare photos and videos of adult animals and their offspring.

Lesson Idea: Demonstrate how the angle of a mirror changes the reflection of a light source.

STANDARDS

SCIENCE	TECHNOLOGY	ENGINEERING	ARTS	MATH	ELA
1-LS3-1	ISTE.3	K-2-ETS1-1	Creating #1		CCSS.ELA-LITERACY.W.1.3
		K-2-ETS1-2	Creating #2		
		K-2-ETS1-3	Creating #3		

SCIENCE & ENGINEERING PRACTICES

Constructing Explanations and Designing Solutions: Make observations (firsthand or from media) to construct an evidence-based account for natural phenomena.

CROSSCUTTING CONCEPTS

Patterns: Patterns in the natural world can be observed, used to describe phenomena, and used as evidence.

TARGET VOCABULARY

alligator

barrier

enclosure

offspring

parents

patterns

physical traits (features)

tortoise

wolf

zoo

MATERIALS

- small mirrors
- empty cereal boxes
- clay
- wrapping paper tubes
- paper towel tubes
- toilet paper tubes

For Testing:

- 3 display boards (representing the zoo barriers)
- animal matching cards (page 140)

LITERACY CONNECTIONS

Are You My Mother?
By P. D. Eastman

Animal Babies
by PiKids

NOTES

STEAM
—IN—
ACTION

DILEMMA ENGAGE

It was just another day at the zoo, until the baby animals went out to play. Baby wolf was tired of being with the adults all day long, so she decided to find some other baby animals to play with. She walked along the enclosures calling out, "Who wants to come out and play with me?" Suddenly, a young tortoise said, "I'm a baby tortoise, and I want to play!" Another voice chimed in, "Me too!" It was a baby gator. The three animal babies played together all afternoon, but now it was getting dark. "We must find our mamas!" they cried out. But there was a problem. They were lost! None of them could remember where their home was located inside the zoo, and none of them were tall enough to see over the enclosure walls. Can you help the babies build a device that will help them look over the walls to find their mothers?

MISSION

Build a device that allows you to see over the barrier walls to match the baby animals to their mothers on the other side.

BLUEPRINT EXPLORE

Provide the Individual Blueprint Design sheet, and ask students to sketch three to four prototypes. Once drawings are complete, have each group decide which design to use to construct the prototype and fill out the Group Blueprint Design sheet. Before providing materials, have students write or verbalize why they chose to construct the prototype they selected and why they feel that the other designs would not work as well.

ENGINEERING TASK	TEST TRIAL	ANALYZE	REDESIGN
Each team will build a device that allows members to see over an obstruction in order to identify the parents of three animal offspring.	The teacher will prepare the testing area by placing one of the adult animal pictures behind each of three barriers. Each team receives three baby animal cards. Teams will use their devices to see over the barrier in order to match the babies to their parents.	Each team will determine if its device allows team members to observe and name the adult animals in each picture behind the barrier. If they can, they will place the matching baby animal in front of the correct barrier. Teams should be allowed to observe the other designs to gather ideas, reflect, and make changes in order to improve their prototypes.	Teams can use a colored pencil to make adjustments to their original design sketches. Teams will present the changes to the teacher for approval before making changes to the prototypes. Then they can get new supplies to rebuild and retest their prototypes.

HELPFUL TIPS

- After the Test Trial, have teams take a gallery walk to view other teams' designs for possible ideas to assist them in the Analyze and Redesign portions of the engineering design process.

- If teams are successful on the first try, encourage them to make their prototypes even more efficient. If it is a scenario in which this is not feasible, distribute team members to other teams to be a support for them in making their prototypes more efficient. Alternatively, at teacher discretion, move students on to the Justification portion of the lesson.

- If after the third test the final prototype is still unsuccessful, have students write how they would start over. These challenges are meant to have students build on what they originally designed. If the design proved to be unsuccessful, encourage a reflection/justification on what they would do if they were allowed to start again from scratch.

REFLECTIONS — EXPLAIN & ELABORATE

AFTER TEST TRIAL 1	Were you able to see over the barrier and match the baby animals to their mothers? Were any of the teams successful at identifying which adult animal was behind the barrier?
ANALYSIS	What changes will you make to your prototype to make it more effective?
AFTER TEST TRIAL 2	Did the changes you made help you to see the adult animal behind the barrier? What were some of the similarities between the successful devices?
ANALYSIS	What changes will you make to your device to improve it?
AFTER TEST TRIAL 3	Were you able to match the baby animals to their mothers?

JUSTIFICATION — EVALUATE

ARTS	Use modeling clay to build a model of one of the three baby animals and its mother.
ELA	Write a story about the adventures the three baby animals had together during their day outside the zoo enclosures.
TECHNOLOGY	Use the Internet to research and create a short presentation about three other adult animals and their offspring.

CAVERNOUS COMMUNICATION

STEAM

SETTING —THE— STAGE

DESIGN CHALLENGE PURPOSE

Use glow sticks to communicate in the dark.

TEACHER DEVELOPMENT

Discuss with students some facts about **caves**. Caves can be cold and wet. Sometimes bats live inside of them. Caves can also be very dark in some places. Prefacing this challenge with a brief discussion about how caves are often cold and very dark will help students further understand the challenge.

Talk also about glow sticks and how they work. To activate a glow stick, it must be cracked to allow the chemicals inside to mix. This causes a chemical reaction that produces heat and light. Freezing a glow stick after the chemical reaction takes place slows down the reaction, which lowers the **temperature** and makes the light dim.

The other aspect of this lesson covers **communication** without sound. Discuss with students different ways to communicate without speaking.

STUDENT DEVELOPMENT

Students will need background information in three areas: glow sticks, caves, and communicating without sound. They will need to understand that glow sticks, once broken, create light and heat through a chemical reaction. You can tell them that the liquids inside mix together when the stick is snapped. The chemical reaction creates light and heat, which users can feel with their hands. Students will need to understand that caves are cold, damp, and dark places where bats sometimes live. Introduce students to American Sign Language and flag signals so that they understand some ways to communicate without sound. Lead a discussion about communicating without speaking. Ask students if they've ever wanted to tell a friend something but didn't want anyone else to hear it? Ask them if they've ever used their hands to point to something they wanted someone to look at. Tell them that if they have done that, they have communicated without making a sound. Explain that when baseball coaches don't want the other team to know what they are going to do, they use hand signals to communicate. Hand signals work when you need to communicate without speaking. Waving your hand could mean hello or goodbye. Pointing your finger could tell someone to go in a certain direction.

Note: Visit the website listed on the inside front cover for more information about American Sign Language and flag signals.

STANDARDS

SCIENCE	TECHNOLOGY	ENGINEERING	ARTS	MATH	ELA
1-PS4-2		K-2-ETS1-1	Creating #1		CCSS.ELA-LITERACY.SL.1.1
1-PS4-4		K-2-ETS1-2	Creating #2		CCSS.ELA-LITERACY.W.1.3
		K-2-ETS1-3	Creating #3		

SCIENCE & ENGINEERING PRACTICES

Constructing Explanations and Designing Solutions: Make observations (firsthand or from media) to construct an evidence-based account for natural phenomena. Use tools and/or materials to design and/or build a device that solves a specific problem or a solution to a specific problem.

CROSSCUTTING CONCEPTS

Cause and Effect: Simple tests can be designed to gather evidence to support or refute student ideas about causes.

TARGET VOCABULARY

cave

communication

glow sticks

temperature

MATERIALS

- dark room
- 3 glow sticks

LITERACY CONNECTIONS

Caves
by Ellen Labrecque

Maritime Signal Flags!
How Boats Speak to
Each Other
by Left Brain Kids

NOTES

S t **E A** m

STEAM IN ACTION

DILEMMA — ENGAGE

Katy and her family want to explore the local cave, but they heard that the cave is full of bats! The bats are easily startled by the bright light from a flashlight and by any sound they hear. Katy and her family need your help to come up with a way to communicate in the dark without speaking.

MISSION

Use glow sticks to communicate the following words without making a sound:

- stop
- go
- left
- right

BLUEPRINT — EXPLORE

Provide the Individual Blueprint Design sheet, and ask students to sketch three to four prototypes. Once drawings are complete, have each group decide which design to use to construct the prototype and fill out the Group Blueprint Design sheet. Before providing materials, have students write or verbalize why they chose to construct the prototype they selected and why they feel that the other designs would not work as well.

ENGINEERING TASK	TEST TRIAL	ANALYZE	REDESIGN
Each team creates a way to use glow sticks to communicate in the dark. *Note:* Two team members should stand across the room from their other team members during the test trials. One half of the team uses the glow sticks to send the signal and the other half of the team writes the message.	Teams will use glow sticks to practice communicating in the dark.	Teams will determine if they were able to clearly send messages using the glow sticks. Teams should be allowed to observe the other teams' signals to gather ideas and make changes to improve their own design.	Teams may need to adjust their signals to improve communication.

HELPFUL TIPS

- After the Test Trial, have teams take a gallery walk to view other teams' designs for possible ideas to assist them in the Analyze and Redesign portions of the engineering design process.

- If teams are successful on the first try, encourage them to make their prototypes even more efficient. If it is a scenario in which this is not feasible, distribute team members to other teams to be a support for them in making their prototypes more efficient. Alternatively, at teacher discretion, move students on to the Justification portion of the lesson.

- If after the third test the final prototype is still unsuccessful, have students write how they would start over. These challenges are meant to have students build on what they originally designed. If the design proved to be unsuccessful, encourage a reflection/ justification on what they would do if they were allowed to start again from scratch.

S t E A m

REFLECTIONS — EXPLAIN & ELABORATE

AFTER TEST TRIAL 1	Were your glow sticks seen clearly? Was your message sent and received correctly?
ANALYSIS	What changes will you make to how you use the glow sticks to communicate to deliver and receive your message correctly?
AFTER TEST TRIAL 2	Were you able to see your team's glow sticks from a distance? Were you able to deliver your message correctly?
ANALYSIS	How can you change the way you use your glow sticks or what your message says to improve your communication?
AFTER TEST TRIAL 3	Was your team successful in communicating your message?

JUSTIFICATION — EVALUATE

ARTS	Create a poster advertising your team's glow stick signals.
ELA	Write a story about an imaginary trip you and a friend took inside a cave. Talk about how you were able to communicate and travel in the dark.

RAPUNZEL, YOUR PRINCE IS CALLING

STEAm

1 HOUR
TIME FOR COMPLETION

SETTING
—THE—
STAGE

DESIGN CHALLENGE PURPOSE

Create a device that uses sound to solve the problem of communicating over a distance.

TEACHER DEVELOPMENT

Since the beginning of time, people have used various tools to communicate with each other. People also use tools to make sound. A conch shell has traditionally been used as a horn. In this challenge, students will be using cups and string to create a communication device much like a telephone. **Sound** is produced by vibrations. The **vibrations** produce sound waves that travel through matter to our **eardrums**.

STUDENT DEVELOPMENT

Students need to understand that sound can travel through different substances such as air and water. The vibrations are what cause the sound.

Lesson Idea: Stretch a rubber band around a cup so that it is pulled tight. Pluck part of the rubber band that is over the cup's opening to demonstrate how the vibrations make a sound. Repeat the demonstration using a loose rubber band. Ask students to discuss the difference in what they hear and see. Ask them to explain what they think caused the difference.

To show how vibrations travel in water, tap a tuning fork on a hard surface. Ask students to closely observe the tuning fork and describe what they see and hear. Have them tell you what they think will happen when you touch the tuning fork to the surface of water in a bowl. Tap the tuning fork on a hard surface again and touch it to a bowl of water. Discuss the results.

STANDARDS

SCIENCE	TECHNOLOGY	ENGINEERING	ARTS	MATH	ELA/LITERACY
1-PS4-4	ISTE.2	K-2-ETS1-1	Creating #1		CSS.ELA-LITERACY.SL.1.1
		K-2-ETS1-2	Creating #2		CCSS.ELA-LITERACY.W.1.4
		K-2-ETS1-3	Creating #3		

SCIENCE & ENGINEERING PRACTICES

Constructing Explanations and Designing Solutions: Use tools and/or materials to design and/or build a device that solves a specific problem or a solution to a specific problem.

CROSSCUTTING CONCEPTS

Influence of Engineering, Technology, and Science on Society and the Natural World: People depend on various technologies in their lives; human life would be very different without technology.

TARGET VOCABULARY

distance

sound wave

vibration

MATERIALS

- string (various colors)
- yarn (various colors)
- various sizes and types of cups (e.g., plastic or Styrofoam)

LITERACY CONNECTIONS

Rapunzel adapted by Paul O. Zelinsky

NOTES

DILEMMA | ENGAGE

Rapunzel has been waving her arms out the tower window, calling for help. The prince can't hear her! He just waves back. He seems to be saying something, but Rapunzel can't hear him. They are just too far apart. She needs to create a device that will allow sound to travel to the prince. All Rapunzel has in the tower is some yarn, some string, and some cups. Help Rapunzel use the materials in the tower to make a device that will help her send a message to the prince using sound.

MISSION

Use the materials to create a device that allows you to communicate over a distance of 10 ft.

BLUEPRINT | EXPLORE

Provide the Individual Blueprint Design sheet, and ask students to sketch three to four prototypes. Once drawings are complete, have each group decide which design to use to construct the prototype and fill out the Group Blueprint Design sheet. Before providing materials, have students write or verbalize why they chose to construct the prototype they selected and why they feel that the other designs would not work as well.

ENGINEERING TASK	**TEST TRIAL**	**ANALYZE**	**REDESIGN**
Each team will build a prototype that uses sound to solve the problem of communicating over a distance of at least 10 ft. *Note:* Teams will need to understand that if the string has slack, it will not vibrate and produce sound.	Students from the teams will stand at least 10 ft. apart. Without raising their voices, they need to communicate to each other using their device. *Note:* The teacher should place tape on the floor to mark where the students will stand 10 ft. apart.	Teams will analyze how clearly they were able to communicate using their prototypes. Teams should be allowed to observe the other designs to gather ideas, reflect, and make changes in order to improve their prototypes.	Teams can use a colored pencil to make adjustments to their original design sketches. Teams will present the changes to the teacher for approval before making changes to the prototypes. Then they can get new supplies to rebuild and retest their prototypes.

 HELPFUL TIPS

- After the Test Trial, have teams take a gallery walk to view other teams' designs for possible ideas to assist them in the Analyze and Redesign portions of the engineering design process.

- If teams are successful on the first try, encourage them to make their prototypes even more efficient. If it is a scenario in which this is not feasible, distribute team members to other teams to be a support for them in making their prototypes more efficient. Alternatively, at teacher discretion, move students on to the Justification portion of the lesson.

- If after the third test the final prototype is still unsuccessful, have students write how they would start over. These challenges are meant to have students build on what they originally designed. If the design proved to be unsuccessful, encourage a reflection/justification on what they would do if they were allowed to start again from scratch.

S T E A m

REFLECTIONS — EXPLAIN & ELABORATE

AFTER TEST TRIAL 1	Was your team able to communicate using your prototype? What materials did successful teams have in common?
ANALYSIS	What materials (if any) will you change in your prototype design? Explain why.
AFTER TEST TRIAL 2	Was your team able to communicate using your prototype? Explain what your design had in common with other teams that were successful. If you were not successful, identify the differences between your prototype and the prototypes of teams that were successful.
ANALYSIS	What materials (if any) will you change in the design of your prototype? Explain why you are making those changes.
AFTER TEST TRIAL 3	What did you learn about successfully communicating over a distance using sound?

JUSTIFICATION — EVALUATE

ELA	Write a short fairy tale about Rapunzel making the "telephone" to talk to the prince.
ARTS	Create a book cover for your fairy tale.
TECHNOLOGY	Use a publishing or art program to design an advertisement for your communication device.

SO YOU THINK RICE CAN DANCE?

2 HOURS
TIME FOR COMPLETION

STEAM

SETTING THE STAGE

DESIGN CHALLENGE PURPOSE

Create a way to make the rice "dance."

TEACHER DEVELOPMENT

Sound is created by vibrations. **Sound vibrations** travel in waves, and those waves can cause movement much like the waves of the ocean. Sound waves can travel through solids, liquids, and gases. This is why you can also hear through solid walls and underwater. **Sound waves** can also be felt, such as the vibration you feel when you are near a bass speaker. The evidence of sound waves can be seen and felt, but the waves themselves are invisible.

Part of the purpose of this design challenge is to have the students design a solution given a list of possible materials. With that in mind, allow students to come

to the conclusion that they can remove the top of a shoebox in order to put their solid material across the top and then cut a hole in the bottom for the hose that they will speak into. Students may need hints, but showing them what to do robs them of opportunities for higher-level thinking. Refrain from making a model for them to follow; instead, ask probing questions to help them figure out how to construct their stage.

Note: To make this challenge more festive, you can show videos of circus acts and play circus music.

STUDENT DEVELOPMENT

Students need to understand that vibrations cause sound. They also need to understand that the vibrations of solid, liquid, or gas molecules create sound waves. Provide students with background knowledge of musical instruments that have visible vibrations (e.g., drums, violin strings, guitar strings).

Note: Visit the website listed on the inside front cover for more information about instruments and vibrations.

STANDARDS

SCIENCE	TECHNOLOGY	ENGINEERING	ARTS	MATH	ELA
1-PS4-1		K-2-ETS1-1	Creating #1		CCSS.ELA-LITERACY.SL.1.4
		K-2-ETS1-2	Creating #2		CCSS.ELA-LITERACY.SL.1.6
		K-2-ETS1-3	Creating #3		
			Performing/ Presenting/ Producing #4, #5, #6		

SCIENCE & ENGINEERING PRACTICES

Planning and Carrying Out Investigations: Plan and conduct investigations collaboratively to produce evidence to answer a question.

CROSSCUTTING CONCEPTS

Cause and Effect: Simple tests can be designed to gather evidence to support or refute student ideas about causes.

TARGET VOCABULARY

sound wave

vibration

MATERIALS

- construction paper
- aluminum foil
- small aquarium hoses/tubing
- pool noodles
- rice
- shoeboxes
- straws
- tape
- wax paper
- plastic wrap
- rubber bands
- scissors
- circus tickets (page 141)

LITERACY CONNECTIONS

The Peach Tree Kids: Circus Fleas by Jennie Chadwick

Flea Circus by Monica Carretero

NOTES

STEAM —IN— ACTION

DILEMMA ENGAGE

Mr. Fred Finklestein owns the Finklestein Fun Flying Flea Circus. His circus travels from town to town entertaining guests with fabulously fit stunt fleas. His flea circus needs a new act that shows off Daredevil Dan and his Daring Dancing Darlings. His problem is that the fleas he has to work with can't jump very high and don't stay on the stage. Can your team build a stage that will help the fleas jump higher and stay on the stage? Teams that build a successful stage will receive free tickets to the flea circus show.

MISSION

Build a stage and make the rice jump along to a song without falling off.

BLUEPRINT EXPLORE

Provide the Individual Blueprint Design sheet, and ask students to sketch three to four prototypes. Once drawings are complete, have each group decide which design to use to construct the prototype and fill out the Group Blueprint Design sheet. Before providing materials, have students write or verbalize why they chose to construct the prototype they selected and why they feel that the other designs would not work as well.

ENGINEERING TASK	TEST TRIAL	ANALYZE	REDESIGN
Each team will build a "stage" and create vibrations that make the "fleas" (rice) move without falling off the stage.	Teams test their stages to see if they can get the fleas to dance without falling off. Encourage students to sing a song for the fleas to dance along to.	Teams need to adjust the level of the vibrations and determine the success of the materials in order to figure out how to make the rice move without falling off the stage. Teams should be allowed to observe the other designs to gather ideas, reflect, and make changes in order to improve their prototypes.	Teams can use a colored pencil to make adjustments to their original design sketches. Teams will present the changes to the teacher for approval before making changes to the prototypes. Then they can get new supplies to rebuild and retest their prototypes.

 HELPFUL TIPS

- After the Test Trial, have teams take a gallery walk to view other teams' designs for possible ideas to assist them in the Analyze and Redesign portions of the engineering design process.

- If teams are successful on the first try, encourage them to make their prototypes even more efficient. If it is a scenario in which this is not feasible, distribute team members to other teams to be a support for them in making their prototypes more efficient. Alternatively, at teacher discretion, move students on to the Justification portion of the lesson.

- If after the third test the final prototype is still unsuccessful, have students write how they would start over. These challenges are meant to have students build on what they originally designed. If the design proved to be unsuccessful, encourage a reflection/ justification on what they would do if they were allowed to start again from scratch.

REFLECTIONS — EXPLAIN & ELABORATE

AFTER TEST TRIAL 1	Did the rice on your stage jump? Did it stay on the stage?
ANALYSIS	What changes can you make to your stage to make the rice jump or vibrate? What material did you use for the top of the stage? Is the stage material pulled tight enough? How did you make sound waves that moved your rice?
AFTER TEST TRIAL 2	Did your rice move to the vibrations of the song?
ANALYSIS	Is your stage material pulled tight enough so that the sound can cause it to vibrate?
AFTER TEST TRIAL 3	Did the fleas stay on your stage and dance during the song?

JUSTIFICATION — EVALUATE

ARTS	Perform a circus act using your prototype.
ELA	Write a one- to two-sentence introduction for the fleas on your stage. Memorize the introduction and use your speaking and listening skills to present it before demonstrating how your stage makes your fleas jump and dance.

THE NAPPING POD

STEAm

SETTING —THE— STAGE

DESIGN CHALLENGE PURPOSE

Design a napping pod prototype that keeps light out and reduces sound so a pet hamster can take a nap.

TEACHER DEVELOPMENT

Sound is created by waves that **vibrate**. **Sound vibrations** travel in waves that move like the waves of the ocean. The waves can bounce off of and travel through solid matter, liquid matter, and gas. This is why you can also hear through solid walls and underwater. **Sound waves** can also be felt, such as the vibration you feel when you are near a bass speaker. Many animals, including hamsters, are **nocturnal**, meaning they are most active at night.

Discuss with students the concept of class pets and what their needs are (e.g., safety, food, water, periods of daylight, and periods of night).

STUDENT DEVELOPMENT

In order to understand why hamsters nap during the day, students will need to know that hamsters are nocturnal. Students will also need to understand that sound and light cause problems with sleep habits. Students need to know that sound waves are received by ears in order for us to hear sound. Understanding how sound **vibration** is received will help them understand how to block it.

Lesson Idea: Tape one end of a 10-inch-long string to the edge of a desk and the other end to a ping-pong ball. Let the ball hang freely. Tap a tuning fork on the leg of the desk and bring it toward the hanging ping-pong ball, touching it slightly. The string should swing wildly and repeatedly, demonstrating sound energy and vibration.

STANDARDS

SCIENCE	TECHNOLOGY	ENGINEERING	ARTS	MATH	ELA
1-PS4-1	ISTE.1	K-2-ETS1-1	Creating #1		CCSS.ELA-LITERACY.SL.1.1,
		K-2-ETS1-2	Creating #2		CCSS.ELA-LITERACY.W.1.7
		K-2-ETS1-3	Creating #3		

SCIENCE & ENGINEERING PRACTICES

Planning and Carrying Out Investigations: Plan and conduct investigations collaboratively to produce evidence to answer a question.

CROSSCUTTING CONCEPTS

Cause and Effect: Simple tests can be designed to gather evidence to support or refute student ideas about causes.

TARGET VOCABULARY

energy

nocturnal

sound-proof

vibration

MATERIALS

- aluminum foil
- shoebox
- cotton
- different types of cloth
- plastic wrap
- other items (crumpled paper, fabric, packing material)
- napping pod certificate (page 142)

For Testing:

- cell phone with recording device and app that shows sound waves and volume or a scientific probe or sensor that can detect sound waves (these can be borrowed from middle or high schools)

LITERACY CONNECTIONS

My First Book About Hamsters
by Molly Davidson

The Science of Sound: Projects and Experiments with Music and Sound Waves
by Steve Parker

NOTES

STEAM
—IN—
ACTION

DILEMMA ENGAGE

Mrs. Yawning has a problem. Some of the pet hamsters in her class are very tired in the middle of the day and need to take a short nap. However, the sound of the students working is keeping the hamsters awake. Mrs. Yawning knows that the hamsters are nocturnal and need to sleep during the day. The sleepy hamsters are cranky!

Mrs. Yawning saw a movie in which adults took naps inside a sleeping pod. The pod kept out the light and the noise. Mrs. Yawning needs your help to make napping pods for the hamsters. The team that creates a pod that allows the least sound in will win an award.

MISSION

Create a napping pod that blocks the most sound. Will your team win an engineering certificate?

BLUEPRINT EXPLORE

Provide the Individual Blueprint Design sheet, and ask students to sketch three to four prototypes. Once drawings are complete, have each group decide which design to use to construct the prototype and fill out the Group Blueprint Design sheet. Before providing materials, have students write or verbalize why they chose to construct the prototype they selected and why they feel that the other designs would not work as well.

ENGINEERING TASK   **TEST TRIAL**   **ANALYZE**   **REDESIGN**

Each team will create a noise-canceling compartment for a hamster.

Each team will place the teacher's phone inside its pod to determine if the pod reduces the amount of sound making its way inside the pod. Teams will compare the level of the sound waves recorded on the phone inside their own pods to the sound waves recorded by other teams.

After reviewing the data that students captured on the phone and comparing it to other teams' results, teams will determine if their napping pods reduced the amount of classroom noise making its way inside.

Teams should be allowed to observe the other designs to gather ideas, reflect, and make changes in order to improve their prototypes.

Teams can use a colored pencil to make adjustments to their original design sketches. Teams will present the changes to the teacher for approval before making changes to the prototypes. Then they can get new supplies to rebuild and retest their prototypes.

HELPFUL TIPS

- After the Test Trial, have teams take a gallery walk to view other teams' designs for possible ideas to assist them in the Analyze and Redesign portions of the engineering design process.

- If teams are successful on the first try, encourage them to make their prototypes even more efficient. If it is a scenario in which this is not feasible, distribute team members to other teams to be a support for them in making their prototypes more efficient. Alternatively, at teacher discretion, move students on to the Justification portion of the lesson.

- If after the third test the final prototype is still unsuccessful, have students write how they would start over. These challenges are meant to have students build on what they originally designed. If the design proved to be unsuccessful, encourage a reflection/ justification on what they would do if they were allowed to start again from scratch.

REFLECTIONS — EXPLAIN & ELABORATE

AFTER TEST TRIAL 1	Was the sound in your pod louder or quieter than the sound in the other teams' pods?
ANALYSIS	How can you keep more sound out of your pod? How can you improve your pod?
AFTER TEST TRIAL 2	Was the sound louder or quieter in your pod this time?
ANALYSIS	Was the sound inside the pod louder or quieter than inside the other teams' pods? What can you do to improve your pod?
AFTER TEST TRIAL 3	Was the sound in your pod louder or quieter than in the other pods?

JUSTIFICATION — EVALUATE

ARTS	Decorate the outside of your napping pod so it is inviting to the hamsters and also blends into its surroundings inside the cage.
ELA	Work together with your team members to research and write a short report about hamsters. Include information about their sleeping habits.

APPENDIX

Lesson Plan–Specific Reproducibles 129

Individual Blueprint Design Sheet 143

Group Blueprint Design Sheet 144

Vocabulary Sheet 145

What I Learned 146

STEAM Job Cards 147

Science Notebook Cover 148

STEAM Rubric 149

Bibliography 151

STEAM Design Challenges Gr. 1 © 2017 Creative Teaching Press

Page ____

Page ____

Page ____

Page ____

Page ____

Page ____

Page ____

Page ____

DEFLATED DEVELOPMENTS
BUILDING CONTRACT

This certifies that

_____, _____,

_____, and _____

have been awarded a contract to build

_____.

_____
Signature

APPROVED

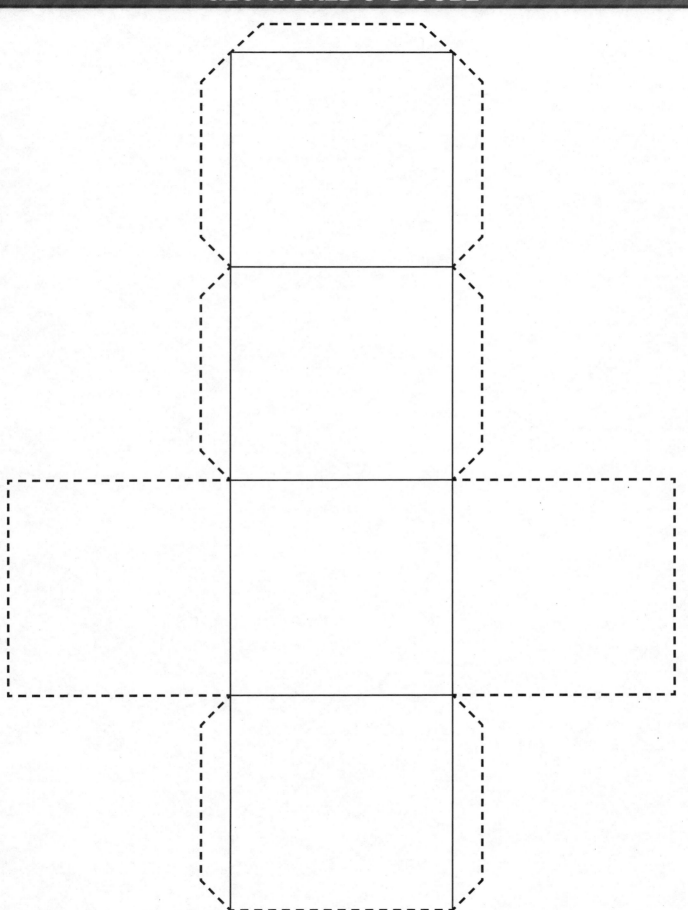

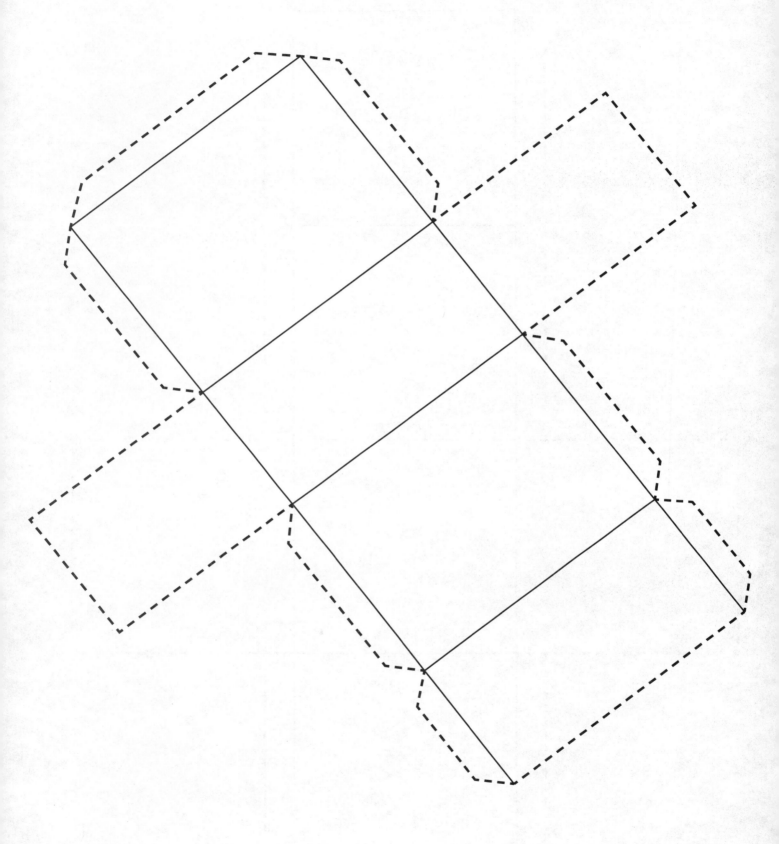

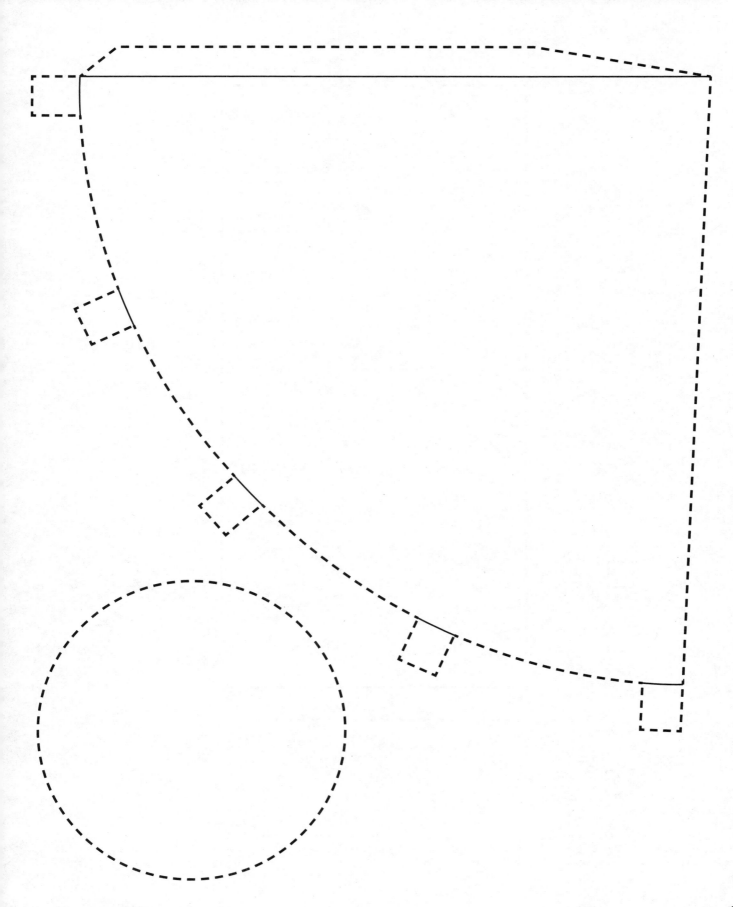

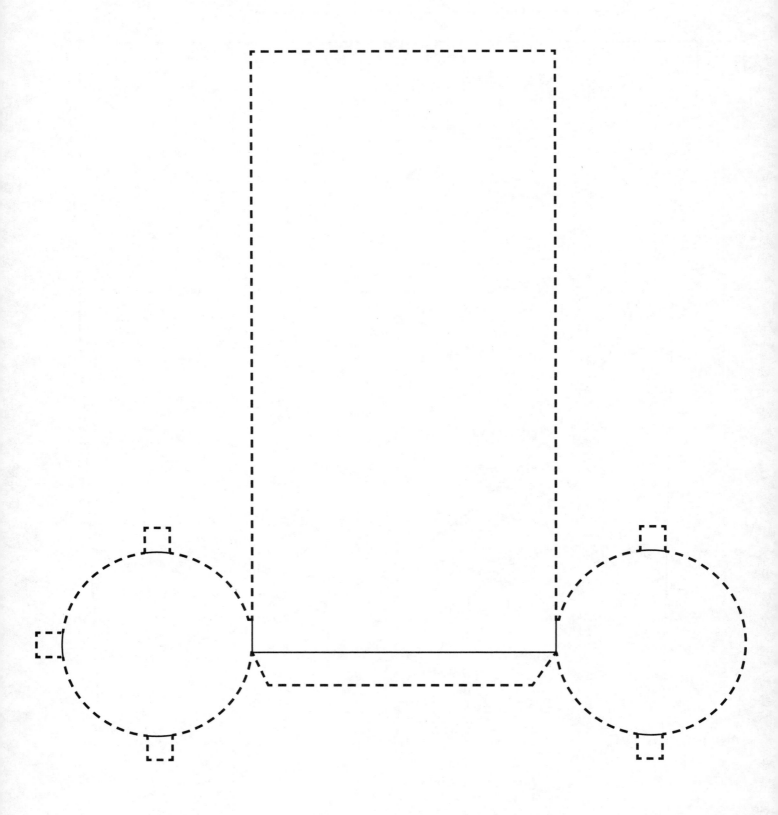

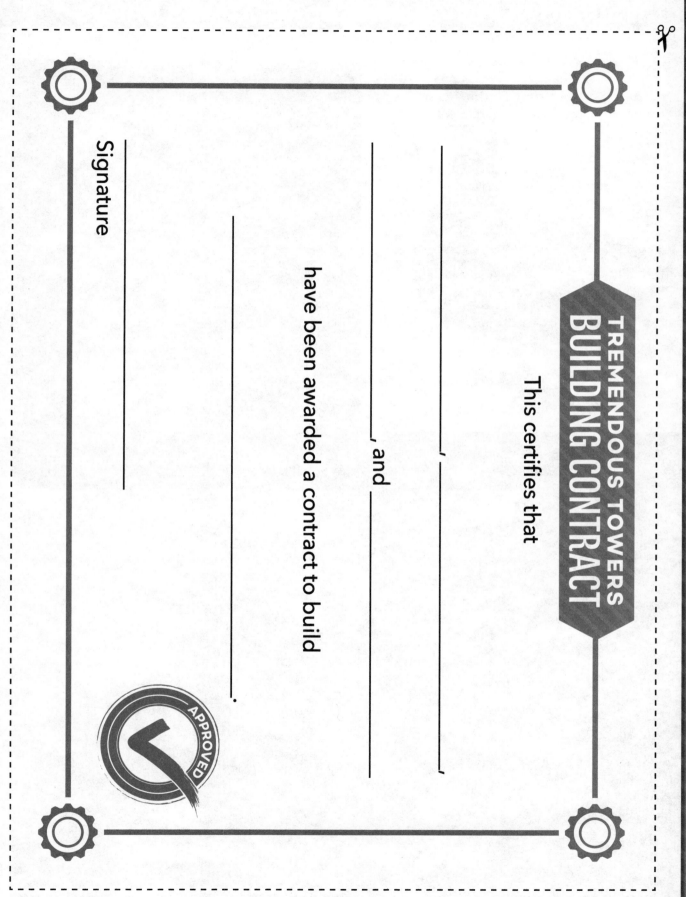

**TREMENDOUS TOWERS
BUILDING CONTRACT**

This certifies that

_____,

and _____

have been awarded a contract to build

_____.

APPROVED

Signature _____

Webbed Feet—Attach to your feet.

Expanding Tail—Attach behind you.

Roar—Use your powerful breath.

Flippers—Attach to your hands or feet.

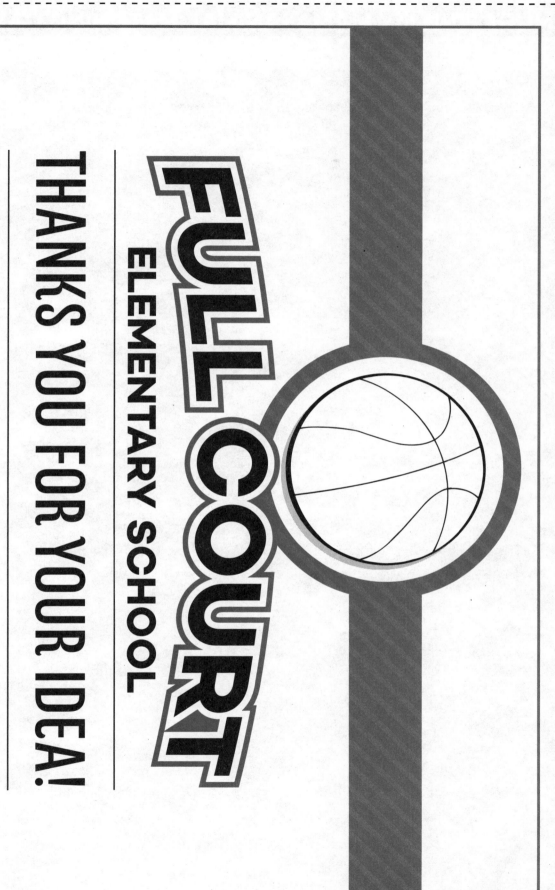

FULL COURT

ELEMENTARY SCHOOL

THANKS YOU FOR YOUR IDEA!

ENGINEERING CERTIFICATE

awarded to

for designing a napping pod for a nocturnal hamster.

THANKS!!

Date:

Teacher:

INDIVIDUAL BLUEPRINT DESIGN SHEET

TEAM MEMBER NAMES	PROS OF DESIGN	CONS OF DESIGN

TEAM REASONING

_____

_____

_____

_____

_____

_____

_____

TEACHER APPROVAL:

 VOCABULARY

VOCABULARY WORD	DEFINITION	DRAW THE MEANING

⚙⚙ WHAT I LEARNED ⚙⚙

Construction Specialist

Description: This person is the one whose design was chosen. This person builds the prototype and is responsible for ensuring that the prototype follows the design rules exactly.

Material Resource Officer

Description: This person is in charge of getting, measuring, and cutting materials for the prototypes. This person assists the construction specialist by getting materials ready and assisting in construction.

Engineering Supervisor

Description: This person is the team leader. This person assists all other team members as needed. This person acts as spokesperson for the team. This person will test the team's prototype.

Cheerleader

Description: This person helps and encourages team members and cheers on success and effort.

My Inventor's Notebook

_____
Name

STEAM DESIGN CHALLENGES TEAM RUBRIC

	EXEMPLARY	PROFICIENT	PROGRESSING	BEGINNING
DESIGN	Team members reach consensus as to which prototype to construct. They complete team blueprint design sheet in which they include their reasons for selecting the team prototype. They include a written or verbal explanation to compare and contrast the prototypes they sketched individually. Prototype is constructed according to specifications in the team blueprint design.	Team members reach consensus as to which prototype to construct. They include their reasons for selecting the prototype but do not include a written or verbal explanation to compare and contrast the prototypes they sketched individually. Prototype is constructed according to the specifications in the team blueprint design.	Team members reach consensus as to which prototype to construct. They include their reasons for selecting the prototype but do not include a written or verbal explanation to compare and contrast the prototypes they sketched individually. Prototype is not constructed according to the specifications of the blueprint design.	Team members reach consensus as to which prototype to construct. They do not include either their reasons for selecting the prototype or a written or verbal explanation to compare and contrast the prototypes they sketched. Prototype is constructed.
TEST	Team tests its prototype. Team records or verbalizes its observations that align with the design challenge. Team makes note of any unique design flaws.	Team tests its prototype and records or verbalizes its observations that align with the design challenge.	Team tests its prototype. Team records or verbalizes observations that do not align with the design challenge.	Team tests its prototype. Team records or verbalizes observations. Team does not record observations.

STEAM DESIGN CHALLENGES TEAM RUBRIC

	EXEMPLARY	PROFICIENT	PROGRESSING	BEGINNING
ANALYZE	Team members participate in an analytic discussion about their testing and observations. They reflect on their design as compared to at least three other teams. They discuss their intended redesign steps, defending their reasoning in their discussion.	Team members participate in an analytic discussion about their testing and observations. They reflect on their design as compared to at least two other teams. They discuss their intended redesign steps.	Team members participate in an analytic discussion about their testing and observations, comparing their design with at least one other team's. They discuss their intended redesign steps.	Team members participate in an analytic discussion about their testing but do not compare their design with another team's. They discuss their intended redesign steps.
REDESIGN	Team redesigns its prototype. Original sketch is altered using a colored pencil to illustrate changes made with supporting reasons.	Team redesigns its prototype. Original sketch is altered using a colored pencil to illustrate changes made.	Team redesigns its prototype. Original sketch is altered to illustrate changes made.	Team redesigns its prototype.
EVALUATE	Team completes a justification activity. Team reflects and makes meaningful connections to the science standards as well as to two of the other STEAM standards addressed in the lesson.	Team completes a justification activity. Team reflects and makes meaningful connections to the science standards as well as to one of the other STEAM standards addressed in the lesson.	Team completes a justification activity. Team reflects and makes meaningful connections to the science standards addressed in the lesson.	Team completes a justification activity. Team makes no connection to the science standards addressed in the lesson.

STEAM Design Challenges Gr. 1 © 2017 Creative Teaching Press

BIBLIOGRAPHY

Ager, Simon. "Maritime Signal Flags." Ominiglot. Accessed September 5, 2016. http://www.omniglot.com/writing/imsf.htm.

"Animal Cams and Videos." San Diego Zoo Kids. Accessed September 25, 2016. http://kids.sandiegozoo.org/animal-cams-videos.

"Baby Animals by Matt, Danny and Kyndal." DragonflyTV. Accessed September 25, 2016. http://pbskids.org/dragonflytv/show/babyanimals.html.

"The Big Dipper." Astronomy for Kids. Accessed September 9, 2016. http://www.dustbunny.com/afk/constellations/bigdipper/.

BrainPOP Jr. Accessed September 12, 2016. https://jr.brainpop.com/.

"Caves." National Geographic Society. Accessed September 5, 2016. http://science.nationalgeographic.com/science/earth/surface-of-the-earth/caves-article/.

Church, Ellen Booth. "Sun Safety: A Summer Safety Activity." Scholastic. Accessed September 22, 2016. http://www.scholastic.com/teachers/lesson-plan/sun-safety-summer-safety-activity.

"Disney's TOMORROWLAND." YouTube. Accessed October 2, 2016. https://www.youtube.com/watch?v=k61moWjT2iM.

A Framework for K-12 Science Education: Practices, Crosscutting Concepts, and Core Ideas. The National Academy of Sciences. Accessed September 26, 2016. https://www.nap.edu/read/13165/chapter/8#87.

"Grow Your Own Grass." Education.com. Accessed September 18, 2016. http://www.education.com/activity/article/The_Grass_Always_Greener/.

Hlusko, Laura. *Plant Defense: Thorns, Smells and Flowers*. The Naturalist Outreach Program. Accessed September 30, 2016. http://blogs.cornell.edu/naturalistoutreach/files/2013/09/Hlusko_TeacherResourceGuideFinal-w0ph2e.pdf.

"Inside Google Workplaces, from Perks to Nap Pods." CBS News. Accessed September 5, 2016. http://www.cbsnews.com/news/inside-google-workplaces-from-perks-to-nap-pods/.

Martin, Pamela. "Your Elementary Unit on Spring: Cross-Curricular Teaching Activities." Bright Hub Education. Accessed September 18, 2016. http://www.brighthubeducation.com/elementary-school-activities/109938-ideas-to-use-for-a-spring-teaching-unit/.

McClure, Bruce. "Come to Know Big and Little Dippers." EarthSky. Accessed September 8, 2016. http://earthsky.org/favorite-star-patterns/big-and-little-dippers-highlight-northern-sky.

Pavia, Audrey. "Understanding Your Hamster's Sleep Schedule." Petcha.com. Accessed August 20, 2016. http://www.smallanimalchannel.com/hamsters/hamster-behavior/hamster-sleep-schedule.aspx.

"Physics for Kids: Basics of Sounds." Ducksters. Accessed September 9, 2016. http://www.ducksters.com/science/sound101.php.

"The Rotation of the Earth." KidsGeo.com. Accessed September 12, 2016. http://www.kidsgeo.com/geography-for-kids/0018-the-rotation-of-the-earth.php.

"Sound Facts." Science Kids. Accessed September 9, 2016. http://www.sciencekids.co.nz/sciencefacts/sound.html.

"Teach Students to Be 'Sun Savvy.'" Education World. Accessed September 22, 2016. http://www.educationworld.com/a_lesson/lesson/lesson008.shtml.

"Teach Your Kids How to Bowl." Teach Kids How. Accessed September 26, 2016. http://www.teachkidshow.com/teach-your-kids-how-to-bowl/.

"Temperature and the Rate of Chemical Reactions." Cool Cosmos. Accessed September 5, 2016. http://coolcosmos.ipac.caltech.edu/page/lesson_temperature_chemical_reactions.

"What Parts Are There to a Plant?" Science NetLinks. Accessed September 6, 2016. http://sciencenetlinks.com/lessons/what-parts-are-there-to-a-plant/.

"Which Animals Use Their Tails to Keep Balance?" Pets on Mom.me. Accessed October 2, 2016. http://animals.mom.me/animals-use-tails-keep-balance-3731.html.